I'M FINE

I'M FINE

A STUDENT PERSPECTIVE ON SUICIDE AND MENTAL HEALTH ON COLLEGE CAMPUSES

EMILY KUMPF

NEW DEGREE PRESS

I'M FINE

A Student Perspective on Suicide and Mental Health on College Campuses

ISBN   978-1-64137-927-4   *Paperback*

          978-1-64137-718-8   *Kindle Ebook*

          978-1-64137-719-5   *Ebook*

DISCLAIMERS

MEDICAL DISCLAIMER

I am writing from a student perspective and therefore am not a licensed professional. The information in this book should NOT substitute advice from a licensed medical professional, a doctor, psychiatrist, or psychologist.

VIEWS EXPRESSED DISCLAIMER

The views and opinions expressed in this book are my own and do not represent entities for which I am affiliated with, including McLean Hospital. The views and opinions of individuals interviewed do not necessarily represent entities for which they are affiliated.

CONTENTS

Dedication

Ryan—aka Bugsy—although you are my younger brother, I look up to you in more ways than you will ever know. Thank you for being brutally honest, wise beyond your years, and resilient as hell. Thank you for being authentically you and inspiring me to do the same in this book.

EMAIL ADDRESS:
imfine@eakumpf.com

WEBSITE:
www.eakumpf.com

"Adolescents and young adults are struggling with an epidemic of depression and suicidality, which, despite advances in neuroscience and mental health, has continued to intensify, unabated. We need to talk about this."

- LISA COYNE, PH.D., CLINICAL AND SCIENTIFIC ADVISORY BOARD, INTERNATIONAL OCD FOUNDATION (IOCDF), FOUNDER AND SENIOR CLINICAL CONSULTANT: MCLEAN OCD INSTITUTE FOR CHILDREN AND ADOLESCENTS (OCDI JR)

"Suicidality and self-harm are real public health crises, particularly among young people. Yet, they are largely misunderstood and often judged. Rather than feeling shame and isolated, people who struggle with suicidality, self-harm, depression, and other problems need to come out of the shadows and interact with less frightened and more compassionate professionals and family members. Emily brings these issues out of the shadows very skillfully."

−ALAN E. FRUZZETTI, PH.D., DIRECTOR, TRAINING IN FAMILY SERVICES, 3EAST PROGRAMS MCLEAN HOSPITAL & DEPARTMENT OF PSYCHIATRY HARVARD MEDICAL SCHOOL

FOREWORD

— — —

Emily is self-referred to therapy, reporting feeling "not like [herself]," with symptoms of anxiety, obsessive-compulsive disorder, rules and distress around eating and exercise, and "high expectations" and perfectionism. She states goals for treatment of "feeling better...love myself more" and to be less critical and more accepting.

That is the language documented in my intake note after first meeting with Emily in November 2017. The assessment section dedicated to Strengths was one of the longest I had written in my then three years of private practice, rattling off a litany that included her intellect, interpersonal skills, history of high achievement, self-directedness, coping skills such as yoga, and robust support network.

My informal first impression: Emily is easy to like. I document in my notes to *monitor for people-pleasing.* Emily immediately struck me as someone who makes other people feel good about themselves. It would be easy to miss the pain behind her wide smile, warm eyes, and insightful statements. Within minutes of meeting Emily, you see her radiating goodness, but what you would not see is the torment and anguish in her head. Emily's self-talk was filled with loathing and punishment. I wanted to banish that mean, bullying voice to Siberia. I had to monitor my tone of voice in session, as my instinct was to shout back at her critical statements, as if I could force Emily to see herself the way others see her if I just argued hard enough.

My own professional background includes working within university counseling centers in the Northeastern and Midwestern regions of the United States. Anxiety is a common cold symptom in these settings. I was struck early in my work there by the high prevalence of trauma and severe mood disorders in this seemingly high-functioning population.

Many of these students, on paper and in the eyes of faculty (and peers and family members), look fine. Emily often looked better than fine—she had a host of friends, well-developed interests, high grades, multiple extracurriculars, and served in campus leadership roles. She even volunteered in the community in her nonexistent free time. Emily's college resumé rivaled many doctoral-level candidates. She clearly loves to connect with others, has perspective and gratitude, is active and adventurous, and, despite what her mean E.D. thoughts told her, is beautiful.

When I met her, Emily was also in agonizing pain. On the outside, she juggled all of these balls seamlessly; on the inside, she was additionally juggling flaming swords in the form of obsessive-compulsive thoughts, eating disordered thoughts, depressive thoughts, and feelings of fear, guilt, and shame.

The *modus operandi* for many high achieving, anxious young adults is to be low maintenance. It is taken for granted that they will meet and often exceed expectations. For Emily and many other high-achieving students, this can create a scenario in which their best is expected (i.e., get the A+ or the 4.0, win the award, get the job, have the social media pictures), and it becomes more relevant to not fail or "dip" below the status quo of their high standards. Often for years their struggles are under the radar. They are no trouble to teachers (or later, to professors, RAs, or roommates) as their symptoms are of the "internalizing" kind. These students don't disrupt class. Their symptoms hurt them and them alone. They are non-squeaky wheels, and get little to no grease.

Emily would report to me what I heard as extraordinary accomplishments in a matter-of-fact tone. In her eyes, she was doing what was expected. She was the person to whom friends went for help and, across settings, was often the one who could be counted on. Our early sessions included discussion about boundaries and assertiveness; it was okay and even necessary to say no, I explained. "Just because you can, doesn't mean you should or have to," I told her. Emily was a helper, a giver, and was also not always comfortable with attention on herself.

Alice Miller famously wrote about *The Drama of the Gifted Child: The Search for the True Self* in 1979, describing the dilemma of intelligent, empathic children. In short, they can be so good at caregiving and performing as expected that they can lose the space to be and find their full selves. It is a book to which therapists often refer, not just for clients, but also for themselves.

I eventually shared with Emily ways that what she expressed resonated with me personally. There were parts of her life that I identified with. I was diagnosed with obsessive-compulsive disorder as an adolescent, struggled with perfectionism and periods of depression, and wondered if there was space to both have mental illness and to be a professional in the field of mental health.

Emily lamented to me ways people in the psychology department cautioned her against disclosing too much of her personal background as she prepared to graduate and go on interviews. They warned her against "mesearch." Many individuals might go into psychology from a desire to help others or perhaps inspiration from aspects of their own life and relationships. But to talk about that openly? That's a no-no. You can be passionate about mental health, but you can't have mental illness.

When I met Emily as a college junior at a prestigious university with a multitude of professional options ahead of her, she had the courage to be both. She spoke her truth as part of workshops about the university counseling center and self-care to other members of Greek life and to incoming first-year students at their orientation. She named her struggles with an eating disorder and suicidal thoughts, being willing to challenge the stigma and to put into words an experience that roughly 15 to 25 percent of college-aged adults will encounter. She advocated for and tried to normalize using counseling services.

Emily shared widely that "it's okay to not be okay," and gave a face and a voice to the notion that you can be a successful student and struggle and ask for help. Emily was not just a survivor of mental illness; she was also becoming a diligent psychology researcher. As a college senior, she designed her own research project to better paint a picture of mental health on college campuses. Suicidal ideation is more common than many administrators might expect among the seemingly privileged and "doing fine" student body. Emily took both the objective data of her research and her subjective experiences as a college student to committees comprised of deans and program directors. Her powerful message to administrators: we may look fine, but we're hurting and need more support.

In many ways, I couldn't ask for a better advocate for mental health than Emily. She challenges the stereotypes of mental health. She looks fine at the same time that she has struggled. Emily is a highly motivated, capable, and successful young woman who has also been in battle with debilitating mental illness. Emily's symptoms checked diagnostic boxes at the same time she was checking off items of academic achievement and personal accomplishment.

Emily—through openly describing her lived experiences and through dedicated efforts to talk to students and to professionals in the field of higher education and mental health—is calling attention to the ways that many young adults who look fine are hurting and being missed by traditional support services.

Mental health workers and academics are often in the ranks of the "fine" as well, feeling overworked and undersupported. Sadly, this can breed a system of mental health assessment and intervention in which only blatant red flags get attended to. In a system with limited resources, someone who at first glance seems "fine" is often not deemed urgent or high-risk enough to intervene. Their hidden pain relies on someone being willing to go deeper, ask more, or not accept that doing okay is good enough. It also requires a climate of safety, support, and openness for students to feel they can honestly disclose ways that they are struggling—without being stigmatized or fearing punitive interventions.

My wish for Emily is that just because she *can* be this powerful and empowered advocate, that it doesn't mean she will *have to* be a lone crusader for much longer. Her book, *I'm Fine*, is a call to arms for anyone connected with university education or mental health, and is also a book on human experience. How often do we hear or ask in polite conversation, "How are you?" And how often does there really feel like space exists to give or to receive a full, genuine answer?

Emily is encouragement incarnate to all of us as human beings to be willing to ask, hear, and share a truth beyond "fine." She inspires me and, if you read her story (and the other narratives she has gathered here), you will be moved, too.

—*Joanna R. Scott*

Licensed Clinical Psychologist

A NOTE FROM
THE AUTHOR

─────

Pieces of this book were written when I was a college student. Other sections were written after graduation, while working full time in a fellowship with children and adolescents at McLean Hospital, a psychiatric affiliate of Harvard Medical School.

In the words of neuroscientist, psychiatrist, and Holocaust survivor Viktor Frankl, "Between stimulus and response there is a space. In that space is our power to choose our response. In our response lies our growth and our freedom."[1]

Protecting my own mental health actually has meant postponing the original timeline for this book. In the past, the perfectionist, inner-critic voice inside of me would have screamed. However, unexpected events relating to the content of this book and my own work in recovery involved

─────

[1]   Frankl, *Man's Search for Meaning*, 1.

accepting that I needed to take time away from writing. I am incredibly grateful to work with editors and a publishing company who were supportive and understanding.

The topics in this book are heavy. They are heavy to think about. They are heavy to read about. They are heavy to write about.

And they are important. Because the less we talk about how to improve suicide prevention and mental health resources, the more we are going to keep losing people.

Any suicide that is mentioned in this book intentionally does not include specific methods or graphic details. That being said, the content still may evoke a range of emotions for you, as a reader. Suicide and mental health are not surface-level topics. It makes sense that you may experience a range of different thoughts and feelings while reading. If at any point you begin to feel overwhelmed, you too can refer to Viktor Frankl's words and take a step back.

At the end of the book, there is a chapter dedicated to resources, hotline phone numbers, and websites with information about suicide prevention and mental health. If I had to choose only one thing that you—the reader—would take away from this book, it would be that there are resources. Help is available. And you are never alone.

HOW TO NAVIGATE
THIS BOOK

———

Overview

Suicide is the second leading cause of death for my age group. Let me say that again—for young people aged eighteen to twenty-four, the second leading cause of mortality is death by suicide.[2] That is the statistic. Not captured by the statistic is the strong emotional impact that suicide has day in and day out on young people who are losing classmates, peers, friends, partners, and siblings to mental health struggles. It is not uncommon to open up Facebook and see memorial posts about people my age who have died by suicide. As a country, we need to be doing better to look at suicide through a public health lens and to address the fragmentation that is our current mental health care system.

---

2   "Suicide." National Institute of Mental Health.

News articles about college students have hit the media hard, referring to a "college student mental health crisis." Articles are quick to highlight the "crisis," rather than focus on potential solutions.

As a college student and a young adult just entering my career in the mental health field, it is evident that there is a problem. However, instead of fixating on the problems, I want to focus on potential solutions. As a society that cares about its young population, what can we be doing *right now* to address what many are deeming to be a mental health crisis? What are the concrete things that schools can be doing *right now* to positively impact the wellbeing of their students?

This book explores these questions and more. It fuses research, the perspectives of leaders in the field, and my lived experiences. My hope is that I can share with you a unique perspective of suicide prevention and mental health on college campuses: a *human perspective* from the eyes of an undergraduate student, researcher, and mental health advocate.

SECTIONS OF THIS BOOK
Depending on who you are (e.g., higher education professional, mental health advocate, university president or provost, parent, professional in the mental health/psychology/public health fields, high school/college/graduate student) and what piques your interest, you may be drawn to specific sections of the book more than others.

PART 1: Post-College Reflections—Unexpected Events: my personal reflections relating to some of the unexpected life events that occurred during the course of writing this book.

PART 2: A Student Perspective: speaks to campus culture, mental health, suicide, research, and mental health advocacy from my perspective as an undergraduate student.

PART 3: What Leaders in the Field Are Saying: features primary interviews with nearly twenty leaders across the country who dedicate their lives to preventing suicide and promoting mental health.

PART 4: My Lived Experiences: dives into my personal experiences with mental health issues, treatment, recovery, healing, and my personal "why" for writing this book.

PART 5: Student Voices and Call to Action: explores what other student leaders around the country are doing, what colleges can do, and insights for students who are interested in mental health advocacy and suicide prevention. If you are a leader from a college or a university reading this book, I strongly encourage you to pay particular attention to this section.

HEALING THROUGH MUSIC

SONG: "THIS IS ME"

ARTIST: KEALA SETTLE

In the "Recovery and Healing" chapter, I speak to the importance of nature, running, meaningful relationships, and music in my life as touchstones for healing. There is something about listening to music—especially live music—that puts my heart at ease.

You will notice names of songs with their corresponding artists sprinkled in select sections throughout the book. My editor, Elina, had the idea to place the name of the song with the artist as a way to set a mood for the section.

As you read, the songs are placed to give you the opportunity to step more fully into my shoes while a college student— these were songs I listened to in both the highs and the lows of recovery while on campus. Each song listed is a small piece of my healing. When you see a song, feel free to listen before or after reading the specific section. The "playlist" of songs is also listed chronologically at the back of the book. And yes—in line with valuing and sharing my true authentic self—I did include a 2007 Miley Cyrus song.

In addition to the songs, my friends' names are intentionally included (with their approval) so that you can be more fully immersed in my college experience. In sharing these details throughout the book, I am hopeful that the reader will gain a better sense of who I really am, not only as a student, researcher, and advocate, but also as a human. And with that, welcome to my journey....

PART I:

POST-COLLEGE REFLECTIONS— UNEXPECTED EVENTS

Writing a book doesn't happen in isolation from one's life. I wrote this section following several intense and unexpected life events that occurred during the writing of this book. I felt this section was extremely important to include.

THE COMPLEXITY
OF SUICIDE

———

SONG: "BEFORE YOU GO"

ARTIST: **LEWIS CAPALDI**

Love is incredibly powerful. During my freshman year of
college, I learned what it meant to fall deeply in love with
another human being. It truly felt like the magic of a movie:
filled with spontaneity, passion, friendship, and a deep sense
of connection. That being said, we both had areas of ourselves
we worked on independently during college. While I went to
therapy for disordered eating (ED) and obsessive-compulsive
disorder (OCD), he went to therapy for post-traumatic stress
disorder (PTSD) and severe flashbacks.

Fast forwarding to life after college, I worked in Massachusetts and he worked in Texas. It was here, while in the midst
of writing a book about suicide, that I learned what it meant
to be in love with someone who intended to end their own
life. And I had absolutely no idea he was about to kill himself
until after he almost did.

I think this highlights the complexity of suicide. You can know the warning signs, the risk factors, the research, and be trained in what to do for a crisis situation. But the thing about suicide and mental illness is that it doesn't discriminate. It can impact anyone and everyone. And even if you know all the warning signs inside and out, you can still miss them.

Five months after my college graduation, my partner abruptly ended our four-year relationship, communicating a need to focus on his future and take time for himself. At the time, I was unaware of the underlying despair growing inside of him.

The night Sammir called to tell me that he had made a plan to kill himself and almost did it two weeks prior, it was 8:00 p.m. and I was walking in Boston Commons. Fear jolted through the entire system of my body. I squatted on the ground, paced my breathing, and watched the squirrels to ground myself back into the present moment. I felt an immense amount of guilt for not recognizing that the person whom I felt closest to in the world had been seconds away from taking his own life.

My ex-boyfriend was extremely hopeless on the call. He acknowledged that his flashbacks, anxiety, and depression were overwhelming. While he stated that he no longer intended to actively hurt himself, his mind still struggled to see a way out of his pain other than suicide. To protect his safety, we created a list of who he would need to call if the urge to attempt intensified, and he promised to go back to therapy.

One of the key assumptions in dialectical behavioral therapy (DBT) is that even if we do not cause our own problems, we need to solve them anyway.[3] I think that is what can feel so unfair about life itself. Everyone is dealt different cards, and no matter hand—whether it is trauma, life circumstances, or the way your brain is wired—you need to be the one to take the steps necessary to *"build a life worth living."*[4]

**SONG: "OCEAN"

ARTIST: **LADY ANTEBELLUM**

My partner from college and I are no longer together, as our lives and futures took different paths. That being said, everything included here is written with his full permission. I learned a lot of lessons from our relationship:

- Being in a relationship with someone who struggles with self-acceptance, suicide, communicating their emotions, trauma, detachment from reality during severe flashbacks, and mental health issues is difficult. It is important to validate yourself as a supportive partner and to recognize that you will also be affected by your partner's suffering.

- Deep empathy in a relationship is a double-edged sword— to have a true understanding of your partner's emotional experience is a gift, but to take on your partner's entire emotional experience is exhausting.

---

3   Linehan, *DBT Skills Training*, 13.

4   Linehan, *DBT Skills Training*, 247.

- If you are living with mental health issues and are in a relationship, it is incredibly important to develop coping skills and rely on close family/friends for support outside of your partner. This means that if your relationship were to end, you would have the tools to manage and cope with your own mental health issues. If you had asked me during my relationship, I would have told you that I *did* lean on others outside of him. I would have told you that I *did* independently manage all my symptoms. Our relationship ended suddenly and unexpectedly. And it wasn't until he was no longer an option to call on that I truly realized the extent to which I leaned on him for support.

- You are not responsible for your partner's suffering or for fixing your partner.

- Your partner is not responsible for your suffering or for fixing you.

- A healthy, stable relationship means that both people in the relationship can love themselves with or without the other person.

It is absolutely critical to promote education on the warning signs of suicide because they are often visible. I truly, 100 percent believe that suicide is preventable and that it is absolutely critical to increase education and awareness. However, it's also important to mention that sometimes the signs aren't as visible. If someone close to you does experience a crisis or dies by suicide and you didn't see warning signs, it is not your fault.

**Note to the reader*: Lewis Capaldi wrote "Before You Go" about his aunt who died by suicide.[5] Lady Antebellum stated that "Ocean" can be interpreted many different ways, but that the overarching theme is "I wish that you could see yourself the way that I see you."[6] Both of the music videos on YouTube sent chills through my body.[78]

---

5   "Lewis Capaldi." *Genius.*

6   "Lady Antebellum." *The Ty Bentli Show.*

7   Lewis Capaldi. "Before You Go."

8   Lady Antebellum. "Ocean."

DR. GREGORY EELLS, PHD.

———

Dr. Gregory Eells was an expert in resilience, worked as the director of Cornell University's counseling center for fifteen years, and served on multiple boards advising college mental health organizations. In his TEDx Talk about resilience, he speaks on the importance of social connection:

> *"As human beings, it is often easy to forget how important our social connections are to us. But biologically, isolation is toxic to the human nervous system. We need each other. We are a part of a super organism of humanity and those connections are essential."*[9]

In August 2019, inspired by his work, I reached out to Greg to learn more about his perspective as a college counseling

———

9   "Cultivating Resilience." TEDxCortland, 2015.

center director and leader in the field. Greg was quick to respond to my email, letting me know that he was interested in participating in an interview. On the day of his interview, I did my typical routine: clocked out of work, walked with my coworker to our cars, and then headed to the gym. In a quiet spot in the parking lot of Planet Fitness, I pulled out a pen, a notebook, and my laptop, anticipating Greg's call.

A friendly, upbeat voice greeted me on the other end of the phone. He spoke with me for twenty minutes about suicide and mental health on college campuses. It was clear he cared deeply about the students he worked with.

Greg asked to have a copy of this book when it was finished, and I let him know I would send him an email with updates in the coming months. In that moment, I was unaware that I would never get to send the email.

Less than three weeks later, at the same time, in the same spot of the gym parking lot, I opened my phone and saw the news on national headlines:

"Gregory Eells died by suicide."

I froze. My entire body began to shake. I gripped the door handle, urgently exiting the car. I tried calling someone close to me, but realized I was physically unable to speak. I paced back and forth in the parking lot, extremely emotional and confused. I had just spoken to him. I had just asked him questions directly about suicide prevention on college campuses, less than a month before he died by suicide.

Hundreds of other college students, counselors, and people across the country were shocked by the loss of such an influential psychologist and leader. His loss impacted the entire college mental health community and made people stop and reflect on the pressures felt by mental health professionals.

Michelle Eells, Dr. Eells's wife, graciously spoke with me. She shared that Greg was so effective in taking care of all the people around him, but struggled to find a way to take care of himself in the same way. Hearing that he was still passionate and still felt strongly about preventing suicide during his interview was a comfort. Michelle's hope is that society will begin to understand how important it is for providers of mental health to also receive support.

There are many unanswered questions surrounding a suicide. Greg spent his life dedicated to caring for everyone around him. And yet he still tragically ended up falling into a state of suffering that he had pulled so many students out of. Mental health professionals are sometimes less likely to seek help in part because of fear and stigma.

No one, including mental health professionals, is immune to suffering. In his interview, Greg spoke to the common humanity aspect of mental health. We *all* experience suffering. We *all* have mental health. We *all* could benefit from acquiring therapeutic skills. We *all* need support at times, including therapists themselves.

His interview in particular made me reflect on the pressure that universities often place on counseling centers to be a "fix-all" solution for human suffering. You can read more from his interview in Part Three. Overall, from his interview I learned:

- Counseling centers are frequently blamed for college suicide deaths. Universities have some responsibility for preventing suicide, but not to the level of blame that is put on them.

- College students have resources and access to mental health services that are not necessarily as readily available to the general population.

- College Leave of Absence policies are incredibly complicated.

- Student voices hold the power to enact change.

Knowing that Greg believed student voices are powerful is affirming. In moments of self-doubt, his words have helped me move forward to keep fighting for change, advocating for additional suicide prevention resources, using my voice, and writing this book.

GLOBAL PANDEMIC

———

**SONG: "WE ARE WARRIORS"

ARTIST: AVRIL LAVIGNE

As I type this, the world is on pause. Life as we have known it has stopped in its tracks. Health care workers are on the front lines risking their lives to protect broader society. Businesses are closed, stay-at-home orders are in place, and masks and toilet paper have suddenly become hot commodities. The timing of writing and releasing this book corresponds with something that we—humanity—are collectively experiencing across the world. These are a few of the headlines that popped up on my social media in the past couple months illustrating the distress, mental health issues, and suicides related to COVID-19:

"NYC emergency doctor dies by suicide, underscoring a secondary danger of the pandemic"[10]

———

10   Iati and Bellware, "NYC emergency doctor dies by suicide."

"The Next Covid Crisis Could Be a Wave of Suicides"[11]

"UN Warns of COVID-19 Pandemic's Heavy Toll on Mental Health: Coronavirus Live Updates"[12]

"Could COVID-19 Finally Destigmatize Mental Illness?"[13]

"Missed milestones, loneliness take a toll on teens' mental health"[14]

"College students experience mental health decline from COVID-19 effects, survey finds. Here's how to get help"[15]

"Coronavirus and the Student Mental Health Crisis"[16]

These are just a few out of hundreds of headlines that indicate people are suffering. By the time you read the words on this page, there unfortunately will most likely be even more headlines. On a national suicide prevention level, universal public health interventions targeting the entire population—combined with selective/indicative interventions that specifically target at-risk individuals—are recommended by public health officials as ways to best prevent suicide during a global pandemic.[17]

---

11   Koons, Griffin, and Court, "The Next Covid Crisis."

12   Dwyer, "Some of the Greatest Causes of Misery."

13   Gold, "Could COVID-19 Finally Destigmatize Mental Illness?"

14   Jackson, "Missed Milestones, Loneliness."

15   Ao, "College Students Experience."

16   Dennon, "Coronavirus and the Student."

17   David Gunnell et al., "Suicide Risk and Prevention," *The Lancet*, 469.

An estimated 14 million college students in the United States were impacted by the pandemic in the United States.[18] Active Minds surveyed 2,086 college students on the impact of COVID-19 for students in April 2020 and found the following:

- Eighty percent of college students report that COVID-19 has negatively impacted their mental health.[19]

- Twenty percent of college students report that their mental health has *significantly worsened* under COVID-19.[20]

- More than half of students (55 percent) say they wouldn't know where to go if they or someone they knew needed professional mental health services right away.[21]

- Forty-eight percent of college students have experienced financial setback due to COVID-19.[22]

- Sixty-nine percent of college students are still hopeful or extremely hopeful about their futures (note: the inverse of this means 31 percent of students surveyed are not hopeful about their futures).[23]

---

18   Dennon, "Coronavirus and the Student."

19   Active Minds, "The Impact of COVID-19."

20   Ibid.

21   Ibid.

22   Ibid.

23   Ibid.

- According to these students, the most important things for school leaders to be thinking about in the short and long term for student mental health during and after the pandemic are:

  - *Increased academic support (leniency, accommodations, flexibility)*
  - *More mental health resources*
  - *Focus on soft skills (empathy, compassion, communication, understanding, validation)*
  - *More opportunities for social connection*
  - *Long-term planning (be prepared to help students heal and recover when they return)*[24]

There are students entering college who may have missed high school milestones: graduation, prom, award ceremonies, senior sports games. There are college students who may have spent time working as an emergency medical technician (EMT) or volunteering on the front lines, and as a result may have experienced significant trauma. There are students who may have lost loved ones to COVID-19.

If you are a leader from a college or university reading this book, proactively preparing for college student mental health is even more crucial now than ever before. If your classes are continuing online, be prepared to best support your students virtually; use the extra time you may have preparing for when students are in-person on campus. Colleges have an opportunity to make changes and start shifting the culture around mental health on campuses.

---

24   Ibid.

My genuine hope is that the suicide rate will not drastically rise as a result of the COVID-19 pandemic, as experts predict.[25] My hope is that society will begin to recognize the importance of mental health and suicide prevention. My hope is that workplaces, health care settings, families, and all schools—elementary schools, middle schools, high schools, and institutions of higher education—will realize the impact of COVID-19 on mental health and make mental health and suicide prevention a top priority. My hope is that when someone asks, "How are you doing?" that people will feel comfortable to give an honest answer beyond: "I'm fine."

*Note: The music video for "We are Warriors" on YouTube by Avril Lavigne is centered around COVID-19 warriors.[26]

---

25   Noguchi, "Act Now."

26   *Avril Lavigne,* "We Are Warriors."

PART II:

A STUDENT PERSPECTIVE

CHAPTER 1:

THE CULTURE OF A COLLEGE CAMPUS

———

SONG: "HEAVY"

ARTIST: LINKIN PARK FEAT. KIIARA

A DAY IN THE LIBRARY

Around me, the library seemed to be buzzing. I glanced up from my computer screen and observed my surroundings. The swim team sat at the table next to me, laughing, trying to piece together memories of a party from the night before. Two engineering students at the end of my table worked diligently on a problem set. At another table, five sorority sisters sat quietly in a circle and discussed moving to the 24/7 area to pull an all-nighter. The table behind me had ordered fried rice and noodles to the library and shared that this was the first meal they had eaten all day. There were people all around me, yet I felt alone.

I looked down at my to-do list and noticed my heart rate increase. My stomach twisted in knots, my thoughts began to spiral, and my inner-critic voice took over:

"You need to get your life together. You need to just get out of your head. Seriously—you need to do better. Stop procrastinating. Just focus. You don't feel okay? Well, you don't have time not to be okay today. You need to just get it together. Everyone else is working and being productive. What is wrong with you?"

The anxious air of the library permeated my body. My chest tightened and my leg started to bounce underneath the table. I pulled out my phone to text a close friend:

"I'm really sorry I've been off. I am so in my head sometimes...."

I hit send.

"Hey Em, how are you?" a student from my statistics class asked as she walked past my table. I quickly tucked my phone away, took a breath, and exclaimed: "Hi!" with a smile on my face. "I have three papers, two exams, and a project due in the next week. But it's fine. I'm fine. Everything is fine."

"THIS IS FINE"

Most college students love memes, so I figured a good way to capture campus culture is to describe one my favorite memes that has been widely circulating across the Internet.

It is of a dog that is sitting at a table surrounded by flames, smiling with his cup of coffee. Above the dog is a little air bubble that says, "This is fine."[27] Clearly, the dog is not fine.

This simple meme so accurately defines the culture on many college campuses. My friends and I often send it to each other when we feel overwhelmed with life. In my experience, the reality of feeling like that dog—metaphorically engulfed in flames—is completely normalized on campus.

Health—mental and physical—is frequently put on the back burner when students are making decisions about where to put their focus. Academics are valued over taking care of yourself. There is an enormous amount of pressure to try to balance friendships, classes, work, family, sleep, relationships, and extracurricular activities while holding the world on your shoulders without it cracking and without you slipping. The later you stay awake in the library, the more meals you skip to study, the longer the hours you work, the "better" you are as a student.

Each college student will have a slightly different interpretation of their campus culture. That being said, it would not be going out on a limb to say that at this moment

---

27   KC Green, "This is Fine."

in our country, the majority of college students are feeling stressed.

DUCK SYNDROME

Have you ever spent time sitting and watching ducks swim along a river? They appear to be gliding peacefully, almost effortlessly, through a body of water. The reality, though, is that their feet are frantically moving beneath the surface to propel them forward.

This concept, known as duck syndrome, was coined at Stanford University to represent college students.[28] I first heard this expression when a friend used it to describe how she felt during her sophomore year.

Spoken or unspoken, this mentality of piling more and more onto your plate is pervasive on campus. The pressure that students put on themselves to do better, to be more productive, while appearing like everything is fine—even when it's not—is the norm. In college, I guided graduate and undergraduate students through a meditation series as a part of my job with our Health Promotion Office. At the end of a class reflection, one student described the culture on campus as a "do or die" mentality. "Do or die" for every paper, every exam, and every project. Taking time to prioritize mental health was viewed as a distraction from school.

---

28   Tiger Sun, "Duck Syndrome and a Culture of Misery."

THE EFFECTS OF CAMPUS CULTURE
ON MENTAL HEALTH

SONG: "THESE MEMORIES"

ARTIST: HOLLOW COVES

For many freshmen entering college, it's their first time living away from home. While some students commute from a neighboring area, others arrive at college jet-lagged after a twenty-hour flight from the opposite side of the world. Students from various countries, cities, and communities travel and arrive at the same place to live together in a shared dorm—bringing distinct experiences, stories, and cultures together.

If you attended college, maybe take a minute to think back to your first week. What were you feeling? What memories come to the forefront of your mind?

For me, it's orientation volunteers in bright yellow colored T-shirts singing and chanting. I think of being eighteen years old, bubbling with excitement at the thought of meeting new people. On that day, I waved to my parents and my younger brother from the window as their car drove away. After lugging the last suitcase up the four flights of stairs to my dorm room, I looked around. It was just me, the four blank walls, and an unprecedented freedom. No one knew my story—I could be fully me—which included knocking on several of the doors in my hall to say hi.

"Hi! My name is Emily and I live in Room 402! What's your name?" I would say as I introduced myself to the people on my hall. Each interaction was slightly different. Isa had her back to the door and turned around with tears welled in her eyes, appearing overwhelmed. In a triple room in the middle of the hall, Rachel had a poster of VJ Day above her bed. On the opposite end of the hall, Mackenzie and Stacey had pushed their beds to the side of the room and invited me to sit on a rug in the middle of their floor with Mia and Maria to play Cards Against Humanity. Marial offered me *de la rosa marzapán* candy that she had brought from her hometown in Mexico. Andrew told me about his love for haunted houses and Fleetwood Mac. My roommate, Maddie, an athlete and engineer, moved in with more shoes than I thought was possible for one person to own.

The connections formed during college can be some of the strongest, most intimate connections that you make in your life. If you really think about it, you are not only living with people your age, but you are also simultaneously entering a common setting—bonded together by the unique intricacies of your university experience and campus culture. At the time, I did not realize when knocking on the doors of my freshman hall how close I would become with the people I met. We came to college with unique life experiences, some of us anxious, some of us excited, as we started this brand-new chapter of life. All of us felt an immediate sense of wanting to create a new community.

Now skip ahead in your memories from the first week to a few months into the year. The initial excitement and newness of college may have died down and the reality of exams, papers, and deadlines hits like a ton of bricks. You may notice the behaviors of other students start to change:

- A close friend from your freshman hall begins to appear sad compared to the semester start. They have a hard time getting out of bed and tell you that they would really like to stay asleep forever, rather than go to class. You tell them you are concerned and suggest that the counseling center may help, but they have no interest in going. *What should you do?*

- New cuts are visible on the wrist of a classmate with whom you are working on a group project. He has mentioned that "family stuff" happening at home has been tough to balance with school recently. *Should you ask him about it? Would that be awkward?*

- Students in your dorm have been drinking on weekends to "blow off steam." But recently, you've noticed that a friend has been getting drunk during the week, too, and is regularly blacking out. *Should you be worried? Many students drink. When does it cross a line?*

- Your own thoughts are racing faster than they have ever before in your life. *You need to do well on this exam because if you don't do well then you will have a poor grade and if you have a poor grade then you won't get a good internship and if you don't get a good internship then you won't get into grad school and if you don't get into grad school then you are failing not only yourself, but also failing your family.* The pressure builds, and suddenly it seems like everyone around you has it together while you sink.

The stress of balancing everything is now more real. Significant mental health issues can be exacerbated or be improved by the culture that exists on a campus.

There is a saying that college is the "best four years of your life." This acknowledges the freedoms, new discoveries, sense of community, explorations, connectedness, personal growth, and "YES" moments that often encapsulate college life. However, this saying fails to acknowledge that there can also be low moments of darkness, loneliness, mental health issues, traumatic life events, and stress during those four years as well. Life ebbs and flows, each semester and each year bringing new experiences.

It took me two full years to come to the realization that the culture on my campus felt unhealthy at times, to recognize that I was feeding into it by not including "take care of yourself" on my to-do list, and to make the decision that I wanted to use my voice to do something about it.

CHAPTER 2:

DEFINING THE PROBLEM

IS THERE A COLLEGE STUDENT
MENTAL HEALTH CRISIS?

SONG: "WAVING THROUGH A WINDOW"

ARTIST: DEAR EVAN HANSEN ORIGINAL BROADWAY CAST

As a college student, my gut reaction to this question is yes, of course there is a mental health crisis on campuses. Tones of anxiety and depression saturate conversations in the library, lecture halls, and club meetings. Self-depreciating humor is a part of our language. Suicidal ideation, depression, anxiety, excessive alcohol use, and mental health issues are often normalized, sometimes romanticized, and even joked about on a college campus. The detrimental effect of campus culture on mental health is all too real.

However, in learning more, I don't think it is a fully accurate statement to say that the crisis exists solely on college campuses. It is important to highlight a statistic that can be easily glossed over, which is that death by suicide is higher for young people who are not in college than for college students.[29] To depict the crisis as occurring solely on college campuses is both inaccurate and misleading. Suicide and mental health concerns affect our entire population of young people, regardless of whether they attend college or not. Suicide and mental health are not a "colleges and universities" only problem. Suicide and mental health affect *everyone*.

That said, it's important to talk about addressing mental health issues on college campuses specifically because colleges exist within a structure that is conducive for allowing changes. They have a unique ability to respond to the overall mental health crisis by working to promote student well-being and prevent suicide on their campuses. University leaders have the ability to allocate funding to mental health resources, implement evidenced-based practices, utilize a comprehensive approach for suicide prevention, and promote a culture that values student well-being. So, the problem? They aren't fully embracing this role.

Mental health concerns arise for the first time for many students during college. In 2017, the American College Health Association (ACHA) survey indicated that nearly 40 percent of college students "felt so depressed the prior year that it was difficult for them to function" and 61 percent of students "felt overwhelming anxiety."[30] In another survey of over sixty thousand students with data from the ACHA, 9.3 percent of college students reported a lifetime history of suicide attempts, 24.3 percent had seriously considered suicide,

---

29   *Suicide Prevention Resource Center*, "Promoting Mental Health," 4.

30   *Time*, "Record Number of College Students."

and nearly 20 percent reported a history of non-suicidal self-injury.[31]

On a global level, the World Health Organization (WHO) World Mental Health International College Student Initiative aims to develop and implement a system for improving prevention and early intervention for mental health problems.[32] As part of this, the WHO surveyed a span of 13,984 first-year students across nineteen colleges in eight countries.[33] Roughly one-third of respondents screened positive for at least one common DSM-IV anxiety, mood, or substance disorder (35.3 percent lifetime prevalence; 31.4 percent twelve-month prevalence).[34]

The high incidence of mental health concerns on college campuses is staggering. The crisis is very apparent.

MENTAL HEALTH IS UNIVERSAL
Before diving further into further research and statistics, I want to describe how I conceptualize constructs of mental health, mental illness, and suicide.

Every single person on this earth has mental health. Just like you have physical health, you also have mental health. There are emotions that are universally experienced by all people—anger, sadness, fear, love, guilt, shame, joy, disgust,

---

31 Liu, "The Prevalence and Predictors."

32 Auerbach et al., "The WHO World Mental Health."

33 Ibid.

34 Ibid.

jealousy, and envy.[35] We all know what it feels like to experience distress, fear, and anxiety because we all are wired with a fear response in our brains. Most of us know what it feels like to experience loss and grieve. And we all have those days where we just don't feel quite like ourselves.

However, not everyone will experience a significant mental health concern in their lifetime. Recent studies estimate that about one in two people throughout the course of their lifetime and one in four students throughout the course of college will experience a significant mental health concern.[36] However *you* feel most comfortable wording it—a significant mental health concern, mental health issue, mental condition, psychiatric disorder, or mental illness—is something that goes beyond the scope of everyday stress. The biopsychosocial theory of development emphasizes that there are biological factors, environmental factors, and psychological factors that influence the development of a mental illness. In addition, for 75 percent of all the people who will experience a mental illness in their lifetime, it will begin before the age of twenty-four.[37] Thus, a mental illness may appear for the first time when a student is in college.

What is the relationship between mental health and suicide? When a person is in a suicidal state, they often don't see another way out. In my eyes, suicide is a permanent escape from temporary pain, an escape from suffering that feels unbearable, and/or an escape from life hardships. If you have

35   Linehan, "DBT Skills Training," 214–223.

36   Active Minds, "Statistics."

37   Ibid.

a mental illness, this doesn't mean that you also automatically have experiences with suicide. Likewise, if you have experiences with suicide, this doesn't mean that you automatically have experiences with depression or mental illness.

However, the American Foundation for Suicide Prevention (AFSP) and other leading organizations state that 90 percent of people who die by suicide have a "diagnosable and potentially treatable mental health condition, even if they don't realize it or are not obtaining treatment."[38] Recently, the Centers for Disease Control and Prevention (CDC) released the statistic that "54 percent of people who die by suicide have no known mental health condition."[39] One study found that 90 percent of college students who die by suicide never sought treatment at college counseling centers.[40] People—human lives—are slipping through the cracks.

I strongly believe that if our country were to prioritize mental health (e.g., fund programs that decrease stigma and increase awareness, provide psychoeducation in schools, teach children skills that build resilience, make quality mental health treatment more accessible, work to increase collaborations between organizations) that we would see the national suicide rate decrease.

---

38 American Foundation for Suicide Prevention, "Ask Dr. Jill."

39 Ibid.

40 Safe Colleges, "Suicide"

THEORIES OF SUICIDE

"What is the pathway through which suicidal thoughts and behaviours develop? What confluence of unique factors lead youth to think about suicide and then act on their suicidal thoughts and attempt to end their lives? The short answer is that currently, we do not know as much as we need to know."[41]

Leading youth suicide researchers wrote this in "Suicide Among Youth: Epidemiology, (Potential) Etiology, and Treatment," an annual research review paper published in the *Journal of Child Psychology, Psychiatry, and Allied Disciplines*.[42]

One of the leading theories of suicide is the interpersonal theory of suicide. The interpersonal theory of suicide assumes that suicide is a result of three factors: 1. thwarted belongingness ("I am alone"), 2. perceived burdensomeness ("I am a burden"), and 3. capability for suicide (i.e., lethal or near lethal suicide attempts).[43] Below are the hypotheses of the theory:

1. "Thwarted belongingness and perceived burdensomeness are proximal and sufficient causes of passive suicidal ideation."
2. "The simultaneous presence of thwarted belongingness and perceived burdensomeness, when perceived as stable and unchanging (i.e., hopelessness regarding these states), is a proximal and sufficient cause of active suicidal desire."

41 Nock et al., "Revealing the Form and Function."

42 Cha et al., "Suicide among Youth," 460–482.

43 Van Orden et al., "The Interpersonal Theory of Suicide," 575–600.

3. "The simultaneous presence of suicidal desire and lowered fear of death serves as the condition under which suicidal desire will transform into suicidal intent."

4. "The outcome of serious suicidal behavior (i.e., lethal or near lethal suicide attempts) is most likely to occur in the context of thwarted belongingness, perceived burdensomeness (and hopelessness regarding both), reduced fear of suicide, and elevated physical pain tolerance."[44]

Another framework that "aims to guide suicide theory, research, and prevention" is the three-step theory (3ST) of suicide.[45] This is an "ideation-to-action" framework that explains the development of suicidal ideation and the progression from ideation to attempts.[46] Below are the three steps of the theory:

1. "Suicidal ideation results from the combination of pain (usually psychological pain) and hopelessness."[47]

2. "Connectedness protects against escalation of suicidal ideation in individuals with both pain and hopelessness."[48]

3. "Progression from ideation to attempts is facilitated by dispositional, acquired, and practical contributors to the capacity to attempt suicide."[49]

---

44   Ibid.

45   Klonsky et al., "Three-Step Theory," 114–129.

46   Ibid.

47   Klonsky et al., "Three-Step Theory," 116.

48   Klonsky er.al, "Three-Step Theory," 124.

49   Klonsky and May, "Three-Step Theory," 125.

Suicidal ideation is defined by "the consideration of or desire to end one's own life."[50] Suicidal ideation can be passive (i.e., thoughts such as *I no longer want to live*") or active (i.e., thoughts such as *I want to kill myself*" or *I plan to use [X method] to kill myself*").[51] A suicide attempt is defined as "an action intended to deliberately end one's own life."[52] According to the CDC, suicide is "death caused by self-directed injurious behavior with intent to die as a result of the behavior."[53]

KEY WORDS:

If you are not familiar with these terms, I encourage you to read below, as gaining a deeper understanding of these words will be useful while reading this book.

Each word is defined by the same source, the "Mental Health & Suicide Prevention Glossary" section of the National Suicide Prevention Lifeline website.[54]

Best Practices: Activities or programs that are in keeping with the best available evidence regarding what is effective.

Comprehensive suicide prevention: Plans that use a multifaceted approach to addressing the problem. For example,

---

50 Cha et al., "Annual Research Review: Suicide Among Youth," 460–482.

51 Ibid.

52 Ibid.

53 Center for Disease Control, "Preventing Suicide."

54 National Suicide Prevention Lifeline, "Mental Health & Suicide Prevention Glossary."

including interventions targeting biopsychosocial, social, and environmental factors.

Contagion: A phenomenon whereby susceptible persons are influenced toward suicidal behavior through knowledge of another person's suicidal acts.

Gatekeepers: People in a community who have face-to-face contact with large numbers of community members as part of their usual routine; they may be trained to identify people at risk of suicide and refer them to treatment or support services as appropriate.

Intervention: A strategy or approach that is intended to prevent an outcome or to alter the course of an existing condition (such as providing lithium for bipolar disorder or strengthening social support in a community).

Means: The instrument or object whereby a self-destructive act is carried out (i.e., firearm, poison, medication).

Means Restriction: Techniques, policies, and procedures designed to reduce access or availability to means and methods of deliberate self-harm.

Methods: Actions or techniques which result in an individual inflicting self-harm (i.e., asphyxiation, overdose, jumping).

Mental Illness: A diagnosable illness characterized by alterations in thinking, mood, or behavior (or some combination thereof) associated with distress that significantly interferes with an individual's cognitive, emotional, or social abilities.

Mental Health: The capacity of people to interact with one another and the environment in ways that promote subjective well-being optimal development and use of mental abilities.

Postvention: A strategy or approach that is implemented after a crisis or traumatic event has occurred.

Prevention: A strategy or approach that reduces the likelihood of risk of onset or delays the onset of adverse health problems or reduces the harm resulting from conditions or behaviors.

Protective Factors: Factors that make it less likely that individuals will develop a disorder. Protective factors may encompass biological, psychological, or social factors in the individual, family, and environment.

Psychology: The science concerned with the individual behavior of humans, including mental and physiological processes related to behavior.

Public Health: The science and art of promoting health, preventing disease, and prolonging life through the organized efforts of society.

Risk Factors: Those factors that make it more likely that individuals will develop a disorder; risk factors may encompass biological, psychological, or social factors in the individual, family, and environment.

Screening: Administration of an assessment tool to identify persons in need of more in-depth evaluation or treatment.

Stakeholders: Entities, including organizations, groups, and individuals, which are affected by and contribute to decisions, consultations, and policies.

Suicide attempt: A potentially self-injurious behavior with a nonfatal outcome, for which there is evidence that the person intended to kill himself or herself. A suicide attempt may or may not result in injuries.

Suicide attempt survivors: Individuals who have survived a prior suicide attempt.

Suicide loss survivors: Family members, significant others, or acquaintances who have experienced the loss of a loved one due to suicide.

It is imperative that we increase our knowledge about mental health and suicide. Gaining an understanding of the above constructs provides a framework to effectively discuss these topics, particularly as we delve into the next chapter.

CHAPTER 3:

SUICIDE (1-800-273-8255)

SONG: "1-800-273-8255"

ARTIST: LOGIC (FEAT. ALESSIA CARA AND KHALID)

*"Life is Worth Living. Lifeline 24-hour
hotline. Call 1-800-273-8255."*

The green and blue sign reflected in the sunlight on the 219-foot bridge, a glimmer of hope located on a structure that bore witness to dark moments of suffering. Lifeline signs on bridges are concrete examples of public health interventions for a leading cause of death worldwide: suicide.

There is a lot we don't know about suicide. Researchers have been conducting studies about suicide for decades. Despite advances in the study, research, and treatment of self-injurious thoughts and behaviors, suicide rates are rising each year for young people. While many hypotheses exist that point to the increased use of social media or to decreases in connectedness as potential causes for these rising suicide rates, there is not one clear answer. We do not concretely know why rates of suicide are increasing.

Our ability to predict who will survive as opposed to who will die by suicide is honestly not much better than flipping a coin. In a meta-analysis of over fifty years of research including, 365 distinct studies, researchers found that there were over 3,428 risk factors and 495 protective factors for predicting suicide.[55] A single risk factor, such as depression alone, was found to be limited in its ability to accurately predict suicide.[56] In other words, there is no singular cause for suicide.

WHAT WE KNOW: STATISTICS

Nevertheless, there is a lot we *do* know about suicide. We know that there are approximately 800,000 people who die by suicide each year globally. This is equivalent to a death every forty seconds. To really understand what this means, maybe take a moment to pause for forty seconds. Set a timer on your phone and sit in silence until the time runs out. Truly feel the weight of the numbers.

The statistics below are from the Centers for Disease Control and Prevention (CDC) Data & Statistics Fatal Injury Report for 2018, as of March 1, 2020.[57] In the United States in 2018:

---

55   American Psychological Association, "After Decades of Research, Science is No Better Able."

56   Franklin et al., "Risk Factors for Suicidal Thoughts and Behaviors."

57   American Foundation for Suicide Prevention, "Suicide Statistics."

- About 1.4 million people attempted suicide.
- About 3.3 million people made a plan to kill themselves.
- About 10.7 million people seriously considered suicide.
- 48,344 people died by suicide.
- Firearms accounted for more than half of suicide deaths.
- Men died by suicide 3.56 times more often than women.
- Suicide is the second leading cause of death for young people ages ten to thirty-four, and the fourth leading cause of death for people ages thirty-five to fifty-four.
- Suicide is the tenth leading cause of death in the United States.
- The suicide rate had increased by 30 percent in the past decade.
- No complete count of suicide attempts data is available in the United States. The CDC gathers data from hospitals on "non-fatal injuries from self-harm" in addition to data from surveys.[58]

For youth, adolescents, and young adults:

- Prevalence rates for suicidal ideation range between 19.8 percent and 24.0 percent.[59][60]
- Over one third of adolescents who experience suicidal ideation attempt suicide.[61] Of the adolescents who attempt suicide, the majority do so within one to two years of ideation onset.[62]

---

58   Ibid.

59   Cha et al., "Annual Research Review: Suicide Among Youth," 460–482.

60   Nock et al., "Suicide and Suicidal Behavior."

61   Nock et al., "Prevalence," 300–310.

62   Glenn et al., "Examining the Course," 971–983.

- "Attempts are typically characterized by specific clinical presentations (e.g., depression/dysthymia, eating disorder, attention-deficit hyperactivity disorder, conduct disorder, intermittent explosive disorder)."[63]
- "Sex presents a now well-established paradox in which adolescent girls are more likely to have experienced suicidal ideation and suicide attempt than boys, but adolescent boys are more likely to die by suicide."[64]
- "Suicide death accounts for 8.5 percent of all deaths among adolescents and young adults around the world (ages fifteen to twenty-nine)."[65]
- Indigenous youth are at higher risk for suicide death.[66]
- LGBTQ+ youth are nearly five times as likely to have attempted suicide compared to heterosexual youth.[67]
- Forty percent of transgender adults reported having made a suicide attempt. Ninety-two percent of these individuals reported having attempted suicide before the age of twenty-five.[68]
- From the Youth Risk Behaviors Survey (YRBS) in 2017, 7.4 percent of youth (grades nine through twelve) reported they had made at least one suicide attempt and 17.2 percent seriously considered attempting suicide.[69]

63 Nock et al., "Prevalence," 300–310.
64 Cha et al., "Annual Research Review: Suicide Among Youth," 460–482.
65 Ibid.
66 Ibid.
67 James, "The Report of the 2015 U.S. Transgender Survey."
68 Ibid.
69 American Foundation for Suicide Prevention, "Statistics."

• "Black students reported highest rate of attempt (9.8 percent) with white students at 6.1 percent."[70]

Do these statistics scare you? Because they petrify me. And these are only the statistics that are reported.

WHAT WE KNOW: PREVENTION

There is a lot we know about suicide beyond its staggering statistics. We know that there are common warning signs for suicide (*listed in the resources section at the back of the book*). Treatment exists for underlying mental health conditions. Public health strategies of prevention, intervention, and postvention have been developed to mitigate suicide risk. These include everything from early primary prevention to creating policies to psychoeducation (e.g., teaching about mental health in primary and secondary schools, hosting awareness campaigns) to training individuals to identify students at risk to planning programs that promote strength and build resilience.

The Suicide Prevention Resource Center is the primary federally-funded resource center for advancing the National Strategy for Suicide Prevention.[71] For suicide prevention to be effective, it needs to comprehensively address various aspects through policies, practices, services, and programs.[72] Below are nine components of preventing suicide and promoting mental health:

---

70 Ibid.

71 Suicide Prevention Resource Center, "About."

72 Suicide Prevention Resource Center, "A Comprehensive Approach."

1. Identify and Assist Persons at Risk
2. Increase Help-Seeking
3. Ensure Access to Effective Mental Health and Suicide Care and Treatment
4. Support Safe Care Transitions and Create Organizational Linkages
5. Respond Effectively to Individuals in Crisis
6. Provide for Immediate and Long-Term Postvention
7. Reduce Access to Means of Suicide
8. Enhance Life Skills and Resilience
9. Foster Connectedness[73]

We know what we need to be doing to be most effective in saving lives. The issue is that, on both the national and collegiate levels, suicide prevention is not being prioritized to the degree that it needs to be—especially given that it is a leading cause of death for young people.

Over 1,000 college students die by suicide each year. These deaths are too often sensationalized by media headlines, which unfortunately may increase risk to additional students. Suicide contagion, or a cluster of suicides, can occur if there is a death by suicide with no postvention. Suicides on college campuses elicit a series of questions. *Why did this happen? Do colleges have a responsibility or role in preventing the suicides on their campuses?*

Far too often, society reacts to tragedy, rather than preventatively implementing a comprehensive approach. If a college fails to have a comprehensive approach to suicide and only

---

73   Ibid.

reacts *after* a student dies, the college is failing to protect their students.

If a college doesn't promote student well-being or provide mental health resources, when mental health issues arise, students may not recognize what is happening to them. In addition, without resources, students won't know how best to help a friend or to help themselves. If a college fails to protect the mental health of their students and prevent suicide, more students will suffer, and ultimately, more students will die.

BEYOND THE STATISTICS

AN UNTOLD STORY

As a preschooler, I was absolutely fascinated with daddy long-legs. These non-spider spiders are older than dinosaurs, with fossils dating back to 400 million years ago. The four-year-olds in my preschool class would run to the back of the field, squat down in the dirt, and examine the intricacies of these unique creatures. We would spend what felt like hours staring and pondering the beauty of the natural world. *"What do you think they think about? Do you think they are happy? Do they have families?"* we would ask each other. It was the truest form of childhood curiosity and innocent exploration.

My mom met one of her closest friends, Cathy Thomas, on that preschool playground. Her son, Willy Alexander "Zander" Thomas, was one of the kids in my class. Growing up, at family-friend barbecues or beach trips, I always saw Zander with a smile on his face. I spent time occasionally babysitting his younger sister Maddie, laughing and playing with her. Flash forward to my junior year in high school. I vividly remember sitting on my bed doing chemistry homework when my dad knocked on my bedroom door. With a look of despair that I had not seen on my dad's face before, he said, "Mom just left to go to the Thomas's."

"Is everything okay?" I asked him.

"No. It's not okay."

Zander was seventeen years old when he took his own life on October 27, 2013.

"When people take their lives, you really don't know why. It's an untold story," Cathy Thomas reflected to me in an interview. Zander was a dedicated teammate for a Triple A hockey team (the highest level of competitive ice hockey), had a strong support system of friends and family, and touched the lives of hundreds of people. His tragic loss came suddenly and unexpectedly.

In interviewing Cathy, she shared about her son:

> *"We don't understand the pain. For him, he could not live with the pain any longer....I've accepted that. I don't want other people to go through the pain that I didn't know he was going through....The other thing too—Zander was here for seventeen years, out of those seventeen*

years, he has touched more people's lives and he did more good than people who have lived like eighty years. It gives me comfort to know that he is remembered by so many of his friends in a very loving, good way, and that he really did a lot of good while he was on Earth. When people hear his name, they always remember him with a smile on his face and warmness in his heart."

There is no right or wrong way to how a person grieves a suicide loss. I asked Cathy what she would want other parents to know who are grieving the loss of a child who has died by suicide. She said that when a parent loses a child, it is something that you cannot even begin to imagine. There is no time frame for grieving or healing. And everyone grieves in their own way. Knowing there are other parents that have gone through similar experiences can be incredibly helpful. She says it is *not* helpful to go down the path of blame. In addition, she says to try to make other siblings' lives as normal as possible, while recognizing that each family member will have a unique grieving process. Cathy aimed to both honor Zander and try to give her three other kids as normal a childhood as possible. Her daughter was only nine years old when Zander died. At first, Cathy thought that she'd never be able to feel joy again. She shared that although life will never be the same, she has hope:

"There will be a time when you will laugh again. There will be a time when you will smile again.

There will be a time when you can hold the memories in your heart. There will be a time when your faith takes over. There will be a time when you are able to see the joys in life again."

For survivors of suicide loss, grief is particularly complex. Unique factors that can make the death challenging include a traumatic aftermath, stigma, shame, and isolation (a mixture of distinct emotions), a need for a reason or "what if" questions, and an increased risk to survivors themselves. [74]

Zander took his life three days after sustaining a concussion from ice hockey. In trying to make sense of their loss and searching for answers, the Thomas family began to learn about the link between traumatic brain injuries and suicide. They discovered the true impact that concussions can have on brain functioning and decision-making. The Thomas family believes that Zander's multiple concussions led to brain damage that ultimately led to his suicide. The UNTOLD Foundation, which was formed a few weeks after Zander's death, is a foundation dedicated to *"educating young athletes and their families, coaches, and communities about the effects of traumatic brain injuries and the mental health issues that can result from either a single concussion or multiple sub-concussive events."* [75] Cathy and her husband, Graham, use their experience to help educate and promote awareness. The UNTOLD Foundation is advised by a scientific board of neuroscientists and psychologists from around the country.

---

74 Harvard Health Publishing, "Left Behind After Suicide."

75 The Untold Foundation, "Our Story."

Suicide continues to touch their lives in various ways. Cathy and Graham receive calls and texts throughout the year from people struggling. Cathy emphasized,

"These kids need help. These people need help."

Some students come into college with a history of self-injurious thoughts or behaviors, either from personal experience or from knowing someone who has experienced suicidal thoughts or behaviors. Others have limited experiences. Every student coming into college brings with them a different relationship to suicide, which is essential to consider when providing support around these issues.

THE POWER OF TAKING A PAUSE

Every single person has a story. The cashier at the grocery store. The man sitting next to you on the bus. The jogger running along the side of the road. The woman who accidentally bumped into you on your commute to work or to class. Every single person you see and interact with has a story. So many instances, in the fast-paced life that is our world, we fail to pause, to listen, and to learn about each other's stories. Each of us exists in our own mind, viewing and experiencing the world from our first-person perspective.

An analogy I really like and sometimes teach in meditation is about the protagonist. We are all the protagonist (i.e., main character) of our own story. All of those around us not in our immediate circles are "extras" in our movie of life. However, what we sometimes fail to realize is that each person around us is *also* the protagonist in their own life. It's a rather meta concept. Essentially, it's the idea that every person around you at any given time is the center of their own world. From a bird's eye perspective, you are the "extra" in every stranger's movie of life. Some of my most impactful interactions have been with the people who would have been the "extras" in my movie, had I not taken my headphones out and tuned into the environment around me.

NO LONGER STRANGERS

My junior year of college, I was walking home from the library to my off-campus house when my eyes locked with a woman who was walking slowly on the pedestrian bridge. It was around ten at night and I was on the phone with my close friend, a typical walk on my way home from campus—except this night wasn't typical.

Looking into the eyes of the woman, I noticed that she had a vacant, thousand-mile-away stare. The stare resembled that of a ghost, as if her body was physically present but her mind lived in a completely different location. In the clinical world, this phenomenon is known as dissociation, although I was not fully aware of this at the time. My gut screamed at me to stop. I dropped my phone and asked her if she was okay. In that moment, she communicated a detailed suicide plan.

Adrenaline shot through my body. I had been trained in Mental Health First Aid. And I knew a lot about suicide from a research perspective. However, I had never been physically present with another person who was about to attempt suicide.

Everyone has their own response to crisis situations. After an initial shock of adrenaline, a calmness came over me, and I encouraged her to sit down next to me. I sat with her as she told me a piece of her story. I told her that she was going to be okay and she was going to make it out on the other side of this. I asked her if she wanted a hug and she squeezed on tight. In that moment, we were no longer strangers.

Other students had walked by us, but no one stopped. Everyone was in their own world, as I had been when I walked across this bridge. Eventually, we both walked off the bridge together toward her home. On the way back to her house, she told me that she hopes I make a difference in this field. She told me that I saved her life. In reality, she saved her own life, and I was just fully present with her to listen to her story. After walking her home to her family, I gave her the crisis hotline numbers and information about local resources in the area. By the time we reached her house, her vacant stare was replaced by one of gratitude. My hope is that moving forward, this woman knows that there are always people to listen and numbers to call in moments of crisis.

ASK QUESTIONS

It took me a few months to walk home from campus without my heartbeat increasing or my eyes darting in all directions. Although no longer as hypervigilant while walking across bridges, my overall awareness has increased substantially. There have been a few instances since my junior year in which a person appears to have been in distress when I have stopped to check in. Sometimes it can feel awkward to ask a stranger if they are okay. However, then I think about the worst and best scenarios of asking that question. The worst scenario could be that they may look at me a little funny and become confused about why I am asking. On the other hand, if they need help, my stopping may impact the course of their life.

Gatekeeper trainings provide in-depth strategies on how to talk to a person who you think may be in distress or may be experiencing thoughts of suicide. In the Mental Health First Aid curriculum, they outline four tips for how to talk to someone about suicide:

1. Look for signs and symptoms (*warning signs listed at the back of the book*).
2. Ask them directly. ("Are you having thoughts of suicide? Are you thinking about killing yourself?")
3. Listen nonjudgmentally (i.e., be kind and compassionate).
4. Let the person know you are concerned and willing to help.[76]

One of the most common myths in suicide prevention is that asking a person if they are suicidal will put the idea in their head. In reality, study after study has shown that this is not true. Asking these questions can be uncomfortable. They are not easy questions to ask. But they are ones that can be lifesaving.

PERSPECTIVE

Does one specific image pop into your head of what a suicidal person looks like? If the answer is yes, begin to challenge

---

76 Mental Health First Aid, "How to Talk."

or expand that image. Suicide spans *all* genders, *all* races, *all* sexualities, *all* ages, *all* cultures, *all* socioeconomic backgrounds, and *all* countries.

My perspectives about suicide and mental health have evolved throughout the course of my four years at college. At the end of my senior year, this passion led me in the direction of public health and psychology. Below is an excerpt I wrote earlier in college, before deciding to write a book on this topic:

"It has been interesting for me to observe, in both the research and mental health promotion settings, how disorders are discussed at conferences, meetings, and presentations as if no one else in the room has experienced a psychiatric disorder. As researchers, statisticians, clinical psychologists, social workers, public health professionals, first responders, doctors, teachers—I believe it is essential to first acknowledge that a stigma exists within the helping profession. I think we would learn a lot more about psychiatric disorders if we learned to acknowledge the stigma that exists so pervasively within the field.

To give an example, this past semester I was at a community mental health meeting for one of my public health classes. Every person in the room spoke of mental illness as if no one in the room was affected: 'What should we do to help them?'

I looked around the room. Most of the people appeared to be a few decades older than me and I didn't know anyone else in the meeting. But I did have personal experiences with the mental health disorder they were discussing. My heartbeat racing, I went back and forth in my head—Speak up? Stay silent?

I raised my hand. 'Hi! I actually am in recovery from an eating disorder and I think...'

Navigating this field and trying to find exactly where I want to make a difference in suicide prevention has not been a linear path. It hasn't been particularly straightforward because the field of mental health promotion and suicide prevention is continuously evolving. Society is beginning to recognize that youth mental health is suffering, and self-injurious thoughts and behaviors are prevalent for this population.

We have been doing research in suicide prevention for over fifty years, yet unlike many other public health epidemics—while research is increasing—suicide rates are as well.

There is no simple answer to suicide. It is complex, multifaceted, and unique. The high prevalence rate and low ability to predict who will die by suicide is a troubling reality. As a starting place for prevention, from the undergraduate perspective at a predominately research-oriented university, I would make the argument that collaboration is key. Epidemiologists, statisticians, clinical psychologists, social workers, public health professionals, doctors, teachers, students, parents—everyone has a role in suicide prevention. Yet in many ways, we are fragmented. We operate in our own roles. There are so many perspectives to suicide prevention. And I think we could all learn a lot about each other from having an open mind."

CHAPTER 4:

RESEARCH AND ADVOCACY

———

As a senior in high school, if you had told me that my entire college experience would be shaped around promoting mental health on my campus, I would have laughed in disbelief. My favorite class in high school was BC calculus and one of my least favorite classes, ironically, was psychology.

Alas, here we are. This chapter speaks to the research, advocacy, and policy experiences on my own campus—living and breathing college student mental health advocacy.

DIVING INTO RESEARCH

SONG: "FOLLOW THE SUN"

ARTIST: XAVIER RUDD

During my first year of college, I was the freshman who stopped and read nearly every posted flyer on the hallway walls of dorms, lecture halls, and libraries. One day, I came across a particular flyer that sparked a burgeoning research interest inside me. A new professor in the clinical psychology department was giving a talk about youth suicide research. I cleared my schedule and went into the presentation, not knowing exactly what to expect. It was this presentation— given by an individual who is now one of my role models— that completely changed the course of my life while at college. I discovered that suicide research in youth and adolescents is an entire field. There are people in the field of psychology who dedicate their entire lives to advancing clinical science in this way. And I was completely in awe.

My undergraduate mentor, Dr. Cassie Glenn, leads the Youth Risk and Resilience Lab (YR²).[77] The YR² Lab studies suicidal and self-injurious behaviors in youth, specifically how these behaviors develop, ways to better predict them, and ultimately how to prevent them.[78] Utilizing both cross-sectional and longitudinal study designs (e.g., ecological momentary assessment), Cassie's lab is rooted in clinical science. As a research assistant for seven of eight semesters in college, I spent time exploring the key questions the lab focuses on:

1. Why does risk for suicide increase drastically during adolescence?
2. Which youth are at greatest risk for suicide?
3. When are youth at greatest risk for suicide?[79]

---

77 Youth Risk + Resilience Lab, "Home."

78 Youth Risk + Resilience Lab, "Research."

79 Ibid.

I feel so incredibly fortunate to have found a mentor who fostered growth, learning, and independence. During my junior year, I asked Cassie about the possibility of doing an independent research project and shared my observations from the student perspective of the following unique paradox: a discrepancy between our clinical psychology department (research) and our University Counseling Center (clinical practice). This is a separation that exists in various settings and appeared to be present at my college. Across the street, the medical campus had one of the best suicide prevention research centers in the entire country. Yet right around the corner on our campus of undergraduates, there was a lack of resources and evidenced-based suicide prevention frameworks.

Before I began research specifically in the area of college mental health, my intuition anecdotally as a student was that of course there is a problem—the vast majority of my peers experienced mental health issues, the waitlist of our counseling center was several weeks long, students were being referred off campus with no means of transportation, and the list could go on.

But I wanted to gather more information. Under Cassie's guidance, I spent a full semester conducting an independent study on mental health and suicide prevention on college campuses. Then in the summer between junior and senior year, I attended the Higher Education Suicide Prevention Coalition Conference, a two-day conference at Penn State University, to learn more about what other universities were doing. I began talking to more students, administrators, and people in general.

Diving deeper into the topic, I learned that the problems on college campuses are even more complex than I initially thought—counseling centers are frequently blamed and handed a capacity that they are unable to care for; there is a dearth of epidemiological longitudinal studies that measure student mental health across time; fragmentation and miscommunication runs rampant between departments; multiple suicide prevention strategies are available to use on college campuses, but colleges are not always using them. Again, the list could go on.

It was very common to hear students complain about mental health services. Many students I spoke with felt their university didn't care about student well-being and viewed the efforts basically as a "joke." However, at the time, there existed no way of quantitatively or qualitatively capturing and measuring these student voices. Because of this and the fact that we did not have a campus-wide mental health screening for students, I built on the information gathered from my independent study and created a thesis research project under my mentor's guidance.

UNDERGRADUATE THESIS

My final undergraduate thesis includes a detailed introduction, method, results, and discussion section. All study procedures were approved by our school's Institutional Review Board (IRB). The study was funded by Psi Chi, the international honor society in psychology, through a Mamie Phipps Diversity research grant. The aims of the study were to:

1. Estimate if a gap exists between students who are <u>currently</u> experiencing clinically significant mental illness symptoms (i.e., screened positive for, or self-reported,

a mental health disorder) and those who are <u>currently</u> receiving mental health treatment.

2. Identify barriers to mental health treatment among students who are currently (i.e., past month) experiencing mental illness symptoms, but aren't currently receiving treatment.

3. Clarify the role of stigma (i.e., self-stigma, perceived stigma, public stigma) as a barrier to mental health treatment.

4. Determine if discrepancies in treatment use and stigma vary across different student groups (e.g., race/ethnicity, international student status, class year, gender identity, and psychiatric disorders).

To summarize my thesis in slightly less academic terminology, the overarching goal of my study was to understand the scope of mental health symptoms, barriers to treatment, and stigma on campus. The study included validated self-report questionnaires to screen for anxiety, depression, substance abuse, self-injurious (nonsuicidal and suicidal) thoughts and behaviors, disordered eating, harmful alcohol consumption, PTSD, mania, insomnia, and panic disorder. In addition to quantitative questionnaires, we included qualitative questions to capture anything that may have been missed.

Although mental health anti-stigma campaigns are quite prevalent, the definition of stigma as a concept is actually quite broad and can be broken down into more detailed constructs. When examining mental illness stigma as a barrier to treatment, it is important to note that there are many discrepancies between how stigma is defined and measured in the field of psychology. The lack of clarity and complexity of the mental illness stigma literature is a major limitation for researchers.[80] Broadly, *stigma* is conceptualized as a theoretical framework based on judgements that some persons or groups are "less than."[81]

Stigma is most frequently classified into different types: public stigma, perceived stigma, and self-stigma. *Public stigma* is defined as the negative attitudes a person may have toward mental illness and encompasses stereotypes, prejudices, and discrimination.[82] *Perceived stigma* is a person's perception about the negative attitudes society has toward mental illness.[83] *Self-stigma* describes the negative beliefs an individual may have toward themselves when associating themselves with mental illness.[84]

Stigma has been found to be a significant barrier to treatment, as evidenced by the over 100 peer-reviewed, empirical articles that have demonstrated such.[85] However, limited research exists about the role stigma may have as a barrier to treatment specifically on college campuses across different populations.

Another way that has helped me understand mental health stigma is thinking about examples:

---

80 Fox et al., "Conceptualizing and Measuring Mental Illness Stigma."

81 Guateneri et al., "Perceived Stigma and Self-Stigma."

82 Corrigan et al., "Challenging the Public Stigma."

83 Guateneri et al., "Perceived Stigma and Self-Stigma."

84 Corrigan et al., "Self-stigma and the 'why try' effect."

85 Clement et al., "What is the Impact."

Public stigma:

- "People with borderline personality disorder are manipulative."
- "People with mental illness are crazy."
- "I think people who are on psychiatric medication can't handle their own problems."

Perceived stigma:

- "I have borderline personality disorder and society thinks people like me are manipulative."
- "Society thinks that those with a mental illness are crazy."
- "Other students hold the belief that those on psychiatric medication cannot handle their own problems."

Self-stigma:

- "I just was diagnosed with borderline personality disorder, so I must be a manipulative person."
- "I have a mental illness, so that means I am crazy."
- "I am on psychiatric medication, which means I cannot handle my own problems."

College students are actually more likely to hold stigma toward themselves (self-stigma) as opposed to having public or perceived stigma toward different groups of people.[86]

---

86 Guarneri et al., "Perceived Stigma and Self-Stigma in College Students."

In addition to validated self-report questionnaires about stigma, we included four response questions to capture the students' perspective from a qualitative angle:

- Do you think that there are a large percentage of students who are experiencing mental health concerns, but are not currently receiving treatment?
- What, if anything, is currently in place at [the university] that promotes your mental health?
- What do you see as the biggest barrier for creating a culture of positive mental health at [the university]?
- Do you believe your mental health has improved, stayed the same, or worsened since entering college?

As a student undergraduate researcher, I had a hypothesis for each of my aims. The study was exploratory in nature, as this was the first time a study was conducted on my campus to specifically assess mental health symptoms, treatment use, and barriers to treatment using validated measures.

WHAT DID THE DATA SHOW?

Of the 940 students who opened the study, 695 met inclusion criteria (e.g., completed at least 60 percent of the study, were ages eighteen to twenty-four, were "attentive" as measured by a validated scale, and completed the study within twenty-four hours of opening the Qualtrics link). Of the 695 students, 524 endorsed current mental health symptoms (75.4 percent of the sample). In other words, roughly three-fourths of the sample. It is important to note that the study was volunteer based, and thus it is possible that students with mental health symptoms self-selected to be in the study.

In a sample of 695 students, these were some of the prevalence rates of <u>current</u> (past month) symptoms for the sample (i.e., not necessarily reflective of prevalence rates on campus) as defined by significant cutoff scores on each measure:

- 36.7 percent screened positive for depression on the Patient Health Questionnaire (PHQ-9).[87]
- 34.4 percent screened positive for anxiety on the Generalized Anxiety Disorder Scale (GAD-7).[88]
- 27.7 percent met criteria for harmful alcohol consumption on the Alcohol Use Disorders Identification Test (AUDIT).[89]
- 24.18 percent screened positive for significant psychological distress on the Kessler-6 scale (K6).[90]
- 21.7 percent endorsed self-injurious thoughts or behaviors on the Self-Injurious Thoughts and Behaviors Questionnaire—Self-Report Form (SITBI-SR).[91]
- 19.7 percent experienced disordered eating as indicated on the Eating Disorder Examination Questionnaire (EDE-Q).[92]
- 16.7 percent screened positive for panic disorder on the Patient Health Questionnaire—Panic Disorder subscale (PANIC-PHQ)[93]

87 Spitzer, Kroenke, and Williams, "Validation and Utility."
88 Spitzer, Williams, and Lowe, "A Brief Measure."
89 Saunders et al., "Development of the Alcohol Use Disorders."
90 Kessler et al., "Screening for Serious Mental Illness."
91 Nock et al., "Self-Injurious Thoughts and Behaviors Interview."
92 Fairburn and Beglin, "Assessment of Eating Disorder Psychopathology."
93 Spitzer, Kroenke, and Williams, "Validation and Utility."

- 10.9 percent screened positive for PTSD on the Primary Care Post-Traumatic Stress Disorder screen for DSM-5 (PC-PTSD-5).[94]

The Self-Injurious Thoughts and Behaviors Interview— Self-Report Form (SITBI-SR) was also used to measure lifetime prevalence rates of self-injurious thoughts and behaviors:[95]

- Passive suicidal ideation: 37%
- Active suicidal ideation: 32%
- Non-suicidal self-injury (NSSI): 26.8%
- Aborted suicide attempt: 9.5%
- Suicide attempt: 6.2%

Of the students who were currently experiencing symptoms, 147 were in treatment (defined as medication or therapy). In other words, 71.9 percent of students who were currently experiencing clinically significant mental illness symptoms were currently NOT receiving psychiatric treatment.

The next step was to determine whether discrepancies in treatment use varied across different student groups (e.g., race/ethnicity, international student status, class year, gender, and psychiatric disorders). For these analyses, the majority group was compared to the minority group. Greater specificity based on treatment seeking among subgroups within the minority group may have made students identifiable, and therefore were combined into one larger minority group. The

94   Prins et al., "The Primary Care PTSD Screen for DSM-5."
95   Nock et al., "Self-Injurious Thoughts and Behaviors Interview."

largest predictors of using mental health treatment included being white (includes both Hispanic and non-Hispanic ethnicity), being a domestic student, and being female.

For the 377 students who were currently experiencing mental health symptoms and NOT currently in treatment, we asked about barriers to treatment.

The most common barrier to therapy was:

- "Stress is normal in college." (48.28%)

The most common barriers to medication was:

- "I have not had any need." (60.74%)

The quantitative scales did not capture any significant differences in treatment use between those who were vs. were not in treatment based on self-stigma, perceived stigma, and public stigma. However, there was an "other" qualitative section which included responses indicating stigma was present. Examples of some of the types of responses include:

- Family/culture looks down on therapy
- Reliance on medication is seen as a form of weakness
- Reliance on others is seen as a failure

We also asked about broad, campus-wide barriers through the question, "What do you see as the biggest barrier for creating a culture of positive mental health at [the university]?"

The biggest barriers were:

- Our culture itself (e.g., our school motto; normalization of serious mental health concerns; romanticization of stress as a point of pride)
- Perceived stigma
- Negative perception of services
- Belief that the university does not care about students
- Perceived lack of resources

Responses varied in length. Some students wrote paragraphs, their frustrations and voice clear: our culture needs to shift.

We also looked at protective factors measured by the question, "What, if anything, is currently in place at [the university] that promotes your mental health?"

The perceived protective factors were:

- Counseling Center/Health Services
- Referral Network
- Friends
- Clubs
- "Nothing"

The only category that was mutually exclusive was "nothing," which frequently came in the form of paragraphs and/or profanity. Fourteen percent of students said that there was nothing on campus that was in place to promote mental health.

Working as a student employee in our Health Promotion Office, I knew that there were things that the university was *trying* to do. The problem? It wasn't always reaching people. It wasn't necessarily what students needed. And it clearly was not enough.

LIMITATIONS

There were limitations to my study. The sample, although representative in class year, international student status, race, and major, was NOT representative in gender (71.7 percent of the sample self-identified as cisgender female). Also, it was cross-sectional, looking at one snapshot in time. Another potential limitation was response bias. The study was volunteer-based, meaning students voluntarily either completed the study for psychology course credit or typed in the link after seeing the colorful flyer with a picture of a brain hanging around campus. Thus, there could be response biases (i.e., the students who took the study may be more inclined to take the study due to having experiences with the topic). It is important to note that even though a student screened positive on a self-report measure, it did not equate to a formal diagnosis by a health care professional. Thus, the prevalence rates were estimates of the sample based on the validated screening measures included in the study.

Originally, I asked Cassie about the possibility of doing a longitudinal study. How impactful would it be to follow student mental health trajectories over time? She laughed and told me to slow down and to wait until graduate school when I would have more time.

Cassie was right about the time commitment of my honors thesis. I spent hours and hours cleaning and analyzing data.

My thesis felt time-equivalent to the work of all of my other classes combined. There were many nights that I was working on SPSS (statistical software) and would look down at the clock in the right-hand corner and notice that the time said 2 a.m.—and I loved it. The final step was dissemination of the results.

ADVOCACY AND THE POWER OF CONCRETE NUMBERS
SONG: "HOW FAR I'LL GO"
ARTIST: AULI'I CRAVALHO

As a psychology major with a focus in clinical psychology, I cared about conducting quality research. As a public health major with a concentration in health policy, I also felt extremely passionate about disseminating results to as many people on campus as possible. Before presenting the results of my thesis, my voice was one anecdote. However, with almost seven hundred different students having completed the study, the numbers spoke. Data screams. Don't get me wrong—I love advocating and using my own voice. But the data-driven nerd in me gets really excited to see numbers.

And when I saw that other people on our campus were paying attention to the numbers from the study, I felt empowered. In the spring of my senior year, I presented my thesis findings and met with various departments, students, and undergraduate classes over twenty times in less than two months. In retrospect, it was a tad excessive. However, as an undergraduate, I was extremely enthusiastic about joining as many discussions as possible, even when I felt a little out of my league as I was asked by professors to guest lecture, lead meetings, and present to people who—on paper—have a lot more influence than me, a student. I was excited to be heard. The numbers showed that there was evidently a problem, and administrators, professors, and deans were taking note.

ECONOMIC RETURNS ON INVESTMENT

At the end of the semester, I presented to a committee of our board of trustees. A board of trustees meeting is exactly how you might imagine it to be. Engraved nametags were handed to each person on the way into the door, glass goblets were filled with water on the table, and an air of formality swept through the room. These were the decision-makers of the university.

Before the day of the important meeting, I spoke with our dean of the College in Arts, Sciences, and Engineering to discuss what information I would be including on the power point and to get my presentation slides preapproved. Everything was set.

On the day of the presentation, in addition to speaking about the results of my study, I included broad recommendations (using examples of what other leading institutions were doing) and information about economic returns on investment.

The Healthy Minds Network, dedicated to researching adolescent and young adult mental health, has an online calculator that predicts economic returns on investment for a specific mental health program or service.[96] After inputting data such as the number of degree-seeking students, number of students to receive services/participate in programming, cost of delivering the proposed service/program, and whether the program/service is treatment-focused (i.e., counseling) or prevention-focused (i.e., the general population), the calculator produces a number for the return on investment for the program or service.[97]

In essence, by investing in college student mental health, the college itself has an opportunity to benefit financially. Losing students to leave of absences, transfers, drop-outs, or suicide ultimately loses money. Thus, by initially investing in a student's health, the return on initial investment is much greater than the loss of a student.

As a college student myself, I experienced guilt including a slide about the economic return on investment our university would get if they took a prevention approach to suicide. To put a numerical value that a school would get from saving a student's life seems wrong. From a bioethical lens, I would want to prevent suicide regardless of how much money it would save a university. It goes without saying that people's lives are more important than money, but in an institution, common truths like this become blurred. Morally, I don't agree with this mindset or practice, however, given that I study health policy and know the importance of return on investment for corporations, I included it.

---

96   Healthy Minds Network. "Research."

97   Healthy Minds Network. "Return on Investment Calculator (R.O.I.)."

It was this single slide on the PowerPoint, calculated with estimates of the return on investment, that got the most questions, attention, and time from the people in the room.

Why? Because the numbers showed that schools—including my college—would benefit financially from economic returns on investing proactively in student mental health and suicide prevention. It contradicts my values to frame student's lives in purely economic terms, but if you are a mental health advocate on your college campus, or a director of a counseling center advocating for more funding, I would highly recommend highlighting this as a key point. At the end of the day, colleges function as a business. To them, return on investment is important—no matter how repugnant that might feel or sound. And if colleges want to see their students succeed, mental health should be taken into consideration as one of the key components.

A few weeks after my presentation, at my graduation ceremony, the woman who had led the board of trustees meeting walked over and embraced me with a hug. She told me that my presentation made her think about the potential reallocation of resources to our counseling center. In this moment, the fact that she was someone of significance standing at the college with a building named after her, and the fact that I was just an undergraduate student, disappeared. We were two humans, who connected over a common goal: improve student mental health and well-being.

ADMINISTRATORS DO CARE

SONG: "YOU'VE GOT THE LOVE"

ARTIST: FLORENCE + THE MACHINE

Money and reputation are clearly important on an institutional level. One misconception I held before meeting, connecting, and forming relationships with administrators working in higher education is that they too valued these institutional needs and reputation over student well-being.

As I attended more meetings, I discovered this belief couldn't be further from the truth. In my personal experience, the people who work in higher education genuinely care about promoting student well-being. Sometimes the awareness or expertise or training is missing. The resources or the funding are not always there. Administrators may not aware of the issues that are so incredibly evident to students. But at the end of the day, I honestly believe the vast majority of people working in higher education want what is best for students, while trying to balance the limitations of working within a system.

POLICIES

As a junior in college, someone close to me at another college was struggling with depression and suicidal ideation. He had been hospitalized as a senior in high school earlier in the year and was now beginning to isolate in his freshman college dorm room, failing classes. Rather than offering support, the college looked at his mental health history, handed him a stack of papers to sign, and told him that he would need to leave or face academic consequences. Thankfully, he had a supportive family to go back to—not all students in this situation are as lucky.

Driven by his experience of feeling "kicked off" campus, I decided to look more into Leave of Absence policies and procedures at my own school. Did students here also feel "kicked off" campus? Would students be punished with "academic consequences" if they didn't agree to sign a form?

In short, I learned that if a student were a risk to themselves or others, their Leave of Absence would be handled by the Center for Student Conflict Management (a.k.a. our conduct office). After a suicide attempt or hospitalization for any mental health crisis, students were handed a form. Like my friend, they too had to sign the form or would be forced to leave campus. The exact wording on the form was: "*I understand that recurring violations of the university's code of conduct may result in suspension or involuntary withdrawal from the university.*"

Paradoxically, the name of this form was titled "Supportive Planning Agreement." After additional conversations with other students, I reached out to our administration. Sitting down with an administrator, I shared my student perspective that the wording on the form wasn't reflective of the proffered university support. I conveyed that this form was seen by students as a punishment for experiencing a mental health crisis, rather than a support. In her office, she spent an hour listening, taking notes on how to change the wording, sharing her perspective, and really trying to understand. It is open conversations and moments like these that motivate my advocacy work. It turns out that Leave of Absence policies on college campuses are very complicated. I'll touch on this more in the primary interviews section.

POSTVENTION

In the midst of advocating for our college to be more proactive in having a plan for approaching suicide, tragedy hit. Two people affiliated with the institution died by suicide during my last semester of college.

The entire student body, faculty, and staff received an email that an undergraduate at our university had died. I didn't personally know this student, but my heart immediately sank. What happened? Why did he feel there was no other option? It was crushing. In the email, the dean hadn't indicated how the student had died. However, a local online news article provided specifics. Reading the article, I was horrified by the level of detail provided. Despite many resources and articles available to journalists encouraging them to depict suicide in the media without mentioning details on methods, this journalist still went in-depth about the methods. The guideline to avoid reporting method details is primarily to decrease contagion, triggers, and other attempts (*note: suicide reporting guidelines are listed in the resources section of the back of the book*).[98] Trying to make sense of why the guidelines were ignored in the larger community and feeling an urge to do something, I walked to campus.

The walk across campus felt heavy. My mind raced, trying to keep pace with my legs that were now mindlessly in a

---

98   Greenstein, "Why Suicide Reporting Guidelines Matter."

light jog, I found myself approaching the student union. I decided to try to meet with the administrator who sent the campus-wide email. Walking up the fourth flight of steps to where the dean's office was located, I wondered if he would be open to listening to my perspective.

Although I had never interacted in person with this dean before, he graciously met with me. I shared my concerns about the potential detrimental effects of a suicide being poorly communicated in the local media, and how detailing methods could lead to contagion, or a cluster of suicides.[99] His response surprised me:

"Well, you can't prevent every suicide." Then, *"Our numbers are actually quite good compared to other colleges."*

However, the dean agreed that including methods in university news outlets would be a bad idea, and I left feeling relieved that there would be supportive reporting on campus. Later that afternoon, I was shocked to read a newly published article by a student-run campus newspaper. They too ended up detailing the methods in what they believed was the best course to raise awareness.

I share this example to demonstrate that sometimes even within mental health awareness and advocacy, there can be well-intentioned efforts that lead to potentially detrimental effects.

---

99   Ibid.

The second student who died had recently graduated. This death was not acknowledged in an email to the student body. However, an email was sent out to select faculty telling them to be aware that students who knew him may be at heightened distress. From a student perspective, sending out an email to a team of people to be aware can be a really good thing. It can be especially helpful if they are trained gatekeepers who have tools to identify students at risk. However, the faculty member who told me about this email relayed that they didn't have adequate training, and didn't know how to best support students. Faculty were being told to be aware and support students, but lacked the tools to carry out these conversations.

The irony is that even within an institution, deep scientific research can be taking place across the street and not be put into practice. My university had one of the best suicide prevention research centers in the country. Yet the gold standard of media reporting of a suicide was not followed. And there existed no comprehensive approach for suicide on our campus. The departments were separate, and communication appeared nonexistent—each entity within its own world.

Fortunately, there is a way to bring worlds together. It involves convening all the stakeholders together in one room. At my school, my friend Annabelle and I decided the best way to achieve this cohesion would be in the form of a mental health task force.

PASSING THE TORCH: MENTAL HEALTH TASK FORCE

Creating a mental health task force is exciting. I sat down at a large, round table in our Health Promotion Office with a mug of coffee filled to the brim, a pad of paper, and my laptop open to the Jed Foundation (JED) resources on how to create a mental health task force on a college campus. Typically, these are the resources utilized by campus leadership (e.g., deans, directors). However, given that our school didn't have a task force yet, my friend and I decided that someone had to do it soon, or more students would continue to suffer. And with words of positive affirmation from our supervisors at the Health Promotion Office, we started a mental health task force.

My friend Annabelle was a public health major who also worked in our Health Promotion Office and was a research assistant in the YR² Lab. Having graduated the same year as me, she now works at the National Institutes of Mental Health (NIMH) researching suicide prevention in medical settings. We mapped out various departments on campus, pitched our plan to our supervisors, and emailed contacts from different entities. Our campus was fragmented, and we wanted to bring people together.

We discussed whether the task force would be a suicide prevention task force or a mental health task force. Ultimately, we realized that there could be more buy-in from faculty members if our focus was broad, so we chose mental health. When we sent out the first email, we weren't sure who was going to come. To our surprise, though, every seat in the classroom on the second floor of our health services building filled up. People cared.

Administrators, students, and faculty were finally together in one room. We held several meetings together in which students' voices were heard. In the meetings, you could feel the divide between students and those working in higher education slowly begin to dissipate. Perspectives were shared from both sides, including what was feasible and what wasn't for our campus.

My final presentation of the year, a month after graduation, was to the mental health task force with recommendations from my perspective on areas the school could focus on. These recommendations were informed by both research and my subjective experiences as a student.

Years of work were condensed into seventeen slides on a Microsoft PowerPoint presentation.

Handing the slides over and metaphorically passing the torch to younger student leaders who would be taking over the mental health task force, I walked across campus with hope in my heart that change was coming for our university. The change would be slow. But it was a start. Regardless of what position a person holds, every single person—students included—can play a role in promoting college mental health and preventing suicide.

PART III:

WHAT LEADERS IN THE FIELD ARE SAYING

I spent four years doing the hustle and bustle of college life, while simultaneously becoming a mental health advocate on my own campus. From my perspective, silos exist in the field of mental health. Researchers conduct research. Clinicians treat patients. Advocates fight for change. Policymakers write briefs. Statisticians run data analysis. Within these disciplines, people may be zoned into their own worlds.

What if everyone took a step back? What if we—as researchers, clinicians, advocates, those with lived experiences, younger voices, older voices, and every single person in this country who is affected by mental health and suicide—took a step back and reimagined mental health after examining it from a bird's-eye view?

Because of the disconnect that appears to exist between sectors, one of the main goals in writing this book is to challenge the idea of staying in one lane. In order to do this, I interviewed nearly twenty leaders in the mental health field to hear from voices other than my own as a college student. There are leaders in the field of college mental health, suicide prevention, public health, psychology, and neuroscience who have been advocating and researching these topics for decades.

The interviews in this next section are with leaders from all over the nation whom I look up to immensely. These are individuals who hold an immeasurable wealth of expertise in many areas related to college student mental health and suicide prevention. Breadth, not necessarily depth, is what you will see in the following section. I intentionally touch on a variety of different perspectives with the full recognition that many of these concepts could be books in and of themselves.

One of the major recurring themes that came up across interviews: collaboration and interdisciplinary work may be the key to making progress in reducing suicide rates. This collaboration requires increased knowledge-sharing among disciplines and stepping out of the usual day-to-day roles—which are not easy things to do. It requires time, energy, and a willingness to challenge currently-held perceptions. I feel grateful to have the opportunity to share the following insights, perspectives, and stories from inspiring leaders working to promote mental health and prevent suicide.

CHAPTER 5:

PROVIDING GOLD STANDARD RESOURCES AND PROGRAMMING

———

SONG: "KEEP YOUR HEAD UP"

ARTIST: BEN HOWARD

THE JED FOUNDATION

I tightened the straps of my black high heels, glanced back at the mirror one final time, and prepared to leave. *Is this what people normally wear to galas?* I thought to myself as I exited my hotel to navigate the streets of New York City with Google Maps out on my phone.

I had never been invited to a gala before, let alone a gala at Cipriani Wall Street, where there would be celebrities and other passionate mental health advocates who make it a part of their life's mission to prevent youth suicide. This was JED's

Annual Gala 2019. As a finalist for the JED Student Voice of Mental Health Award, I was invited to attend.

Entering the building, I paused to take in the atmosphere. An enormous glass chandelier hung from the ceiling, Brittany Snow (who I had only ever seen in movies such as *Pitch Perfect*) walked by, and hundreds of people were gathered by cocktails bars. I smiled with excitement at the same time that I felt my chest tighten. This was not my natural element. In that moment, I made a choice: "act opposite" to my anxiety, follow my excitement, and talk to as many people, students, and leaders as possible.

A RESPONSIBILITY TO TAKE ACTION

As John MacPhee, CEO of JED, said during our interview, "I think a high school, a middle school, an employer, a faith community, prisons, jails, small towns, maybe even cities—any community that has members and has the ability to implement approaches that can reduce risk [self-harm and suicide] has a responsibility to do so."

SETTING UP A FRAMEWORK

Donna and Phil Satow lost their son, Jed, to suicide in 1998. Seeing as at the time that there was no framework for approaching suicide prevention on college campuses, they started the Jed Foundation. JED is the leading organization in the nation dedicated to youth mental health.[100] They have worked with hundreds of high schools and colleges to support

---

100 *The Jed Foundation*, "Who We Are"

programming to promote mental health and reduce risks for substance misuse and suicide. Their efforts have reached millions of students via hundreds of schools. Students need to learn skills to help themselves and help those around them. JED provides a structure to foster growth of new skills, raise awareness, and build supportive communities.

As mentioned in the "Mental Health Advocacy" chapter, my friend Annabelle and I used available online resources from JED to start a mental health task force at our school. The main resource that we looked through was "A Guide to Campus Mental Health Action Planning" that gives an in-depth description for universities on how to create momentum, strategically plan and promote mental health, and prevent suicide on college campuses.[101] A comprehensive approach to suicide prevention and promoting mental health on college campuses connects all seven key components of the model below:

- *Develop life skills*
- *Promote social connectedness*
- *Identify students at risk*
- *Increase help-seeking behavior*
- *Provide substance abuse and mental health services*
- *Follow crisis management procedures*
- *Restrict access to potentially lethal means*[102]

There is a lot we know that colleges and universities should be doing. But "before we even get to what a school should do," John emphasized, "a school has to be set up for success."

---

101 *The Jed Foundation*, "Campus Mental Health Action Planning"

102 *The Jed Foundation*, "Who We Are"

ALL VOICES AT THE TABLE

What does it mean for a school to be set up for success? According to John MacPhee, student mental health needs to be a declared priority, with leadership forming an interdisciplinary team of people to oversee mental health planning. Leadership—from a provost or president of a university—can make the difference on whether or not adequate resources and attention are allocated toward mental health.

In addition to leadership from those decision-makers, it is also absolutely essential to have all voices present at the table. This includes students, faculty, athletics, facilities, disability resources center, residential life, campus security, legal team, and more. Like any other business endeavor approach, the interdisciplinary team should construct a written plan about how to reduce risk for mental health issues, substance abuse, and suicide, to be updated each year. A school needs to support the idea that mental health belongs to *everybody,* rather than solely a counseling or a health center. Overall, schools have a responsibility to take action in a thoughtful and comprehensive way.

INVESTING IN MENTAL HEALTH

If all of the voices are not included at the table, students may suffer. John MacPhee explained one potential example to me:

Imagine there is a roof on a building that students like to hang out on. Over the past few years, several students have died from jumping off this building. The building currently has no barriers. A mental health team argues that it is necessary for barriers or plexiglass to be installed so that potentially suicidal students will be prevented from accessing the roof as a means for suicide. The decision on whether to implement such building changes lies within the facilities department. However, the facilities department may not want to spend half a million dollars on new barriers. If they are not part of the mental health task force, they may falsely believe that if a student wants to die by suicide, they will find a different method. Yet according to John MacPhee, we know that barriers and restricting access to lethal means are effective in preventing death by suicide.

CHANGE IS SLOW...BUT STEADY

I then asked how one would begin to shift the culture to prioritize mental health. He highlighted a common theme felt by both students and universities: "Change in a culture is slow. Colleges have been around for decades and often structural change takes time." However, he revealed that getting engagement from top leaders at a university can come from student advocacy, consultation with experts, and comparison to what is working for other schools. He also spoke to the return on investing in mental health.

One of the main contributors to student dropout rates is money, academics, death in the family, alcohol or drugs, or other emotional stressors. Investing in mental health proactively benefits a college in the long run because retention and graduation rates increase.

WITNESSING TRANSFORMATIONS

John MacPhee described himself as a shy, anxious college student who struggled with drinking and initially failed out of college. While at school in the late 1980s, he was not consciously aware of being depressed. "I didn't have a language or an understanding of what was going on with me," he told me.

Today, he feels lucky to work in a space that is supportive of young adults and teenagers. As part of his job, he has seen outcomes in personal stories and in university mental health transformations. For example, JED recommended that a college implement a 24/7 crisis service, and the school put one in place. One person approached him and said that watching a JED video saved his life. He has watched his daughters change from young teenagers to young adults during his time working with JED.

For transformation to occur, John MacPhee highlighted the need for "upstream public health prevention in addition to access to care and treatment" and emphasized the importance of social connectedness in ways that are important to identity. College students have intersectional identities—cultural, religious, sexuality, gender, ability—just to name a few. Finding meaningful connections and spaces on campus where students can fully express their true identities is absolutely imperative to fostering positive mental health.

JED STORYTELLERS

One example of how JED fosters positive mental health is a program called JED Storytellers. JED storytellers share their personal experiences to show just how powerful " stories can be in reducing shame, prejudice, and secrecy."[103] Through these stories, "we find compassion and inspiration and the understanding that there is hope."[104]

One such JED storyteller, and one of the inspiring people I talked with the night of the JED gala, was Zak Sandler, a "mental health advocate with a musical twist." Zak has played piano on Broadway for *WICKED, MEAN GIRLS, Motown the Musical,* and *The Color Purple.* He has also written a musical about his bipolar called *INSIDE MY HEAD,* in which he personifies his depression as Doug, his mania as Marc, and his paranoia as Patty. Zak feels fortunate that he connected with JED and got to know the many "wonderful staff there," including John MacPhee. Zak trained for the JED Storytellers program with a wonderful coach from *The Moth Podcast,* Bonnie Levison, to "help him tell his story in a brand-new way." I reconnected with Zak a year after the gala, and he graciously shared his perspective. He began by posing this question to the readers of this book:

"What if I told you that the point of life is to be happy?"

He continued:

"My parents are both mental health professionals—a psychiatrist and a social worker—so when I was a kid, we talked about feelings a lot. Well, my feelings, not theirs. And some feelings, like anger and guilt, felt off-limits. As I remember it, my parents only raised their voices one time in eighteen years.

---

103 The Jed Foundation, "Storytellers"
104 Ibid.

It wasn't until I was thirty-three that I learned to express my anger and became aware of my pervading feelings of guilt in romantic relationships. I still have a long way to go in terms of seeing, hearing, validating, and balancing my emotions.

"When I got to college, I didn't have a clear understanding of bipolar, or the knowledge that it ran in my family. So when I had my first manic episode, junior year, I was totally unaware of what was happening. I didn't think anything was wrong until a school psychiatrist ordered me to go to the hospital. 'Why?' I exclaimed. 'This is the best I've ever felt!'

"For years, I told almost no one. I lived in fear. My parents even convinced the doctors to change my diagnosis from 'bipolar' to 'mood disorder, not otherwise specified,' because they were afraid I wouldn't be able to get a job or health insurance due to my preexisting condition. It wasn't until my second manic episode and hospitalization, nine years later, that I finally accepted my bipolar, spoke out, and wrote a musical about it.

"I am particularly passionate about helping college students, because my first manic episode occurred while I was in college. Had I known more about bipolar when I got to school, I'm convinced I could have avoided the traumas of the hospital.

"My hope is that *INSIDE MY HEAD*, my musical about my bipolar, raises awareness on campuses and opens conversations both inside ourselves, and across institutions. In addition to performing the musical, I lead educational workshops:

'Emotional Transparency' focuses on being honest and specific when we're asked the often meaningless question, 'How are you?' What would your reaction be if someone told you 'I'm feeling curious and joyful'? How would you feel after telling the cashier 'I've had a really rough day'?

"My other favorite workshop is 'Inside *Your* Head,' where I help people visualize their emotions and draw them as people, animals, and anthropomorphized objects. This allows us to have real, internal conversations between our inner parent and our inner children. Our inner parent is the part of our cerebral cortex that responds to the inner children we all have—our emotions.

"I used to throw around the word 'crazy' a lot, but now I avoid it, and I don't say 'mental illness' or 'bipolar disorder.' I think these terms lend a negative and stigmatizing tone to the conversation, and imply there's something wrong with me. I say 'mental conditions' and simply 'bipolar.'

"I believe that the *real* 'mental illness' is the internal conflict we all feel at times—when different parts of our brains rage against each other, speak out of turn, and play discordantly. This occurs when our emotions—our inner children—throw tantrums, play rough, and try in various ways to get our attention. The cure to the 'illness' is to develop the skills we need to rebalance internally. I'm thirty-four years old, and though I've only just started, I already feel so much happier. I recommend it to everyone. In fact, I would say that the future of the world depends on it.

"When we balance our emotions, we feel happy. And when we feel happy, we're more able to help *other* people feel happy. And that's the point of life, isn't it?

"We can *all* be part of this movement. Let's build a world where we can own our mental health stories, and approach the conversation from a place of unity and love. Let's illuminate the mind.

"Love and Light to everyone reading this, and may our message reverberate far and wide...."

(More information on Zak's storyteller video and how to connect with Zak is in the resources section.)

MOBILIZING COMMUNITIES

One goal of JED is to promote a comprehensive suicide prevention framework beyond the college level to other areas in a community, including at institutions such as churches, organizations, and companies and in small tight-knit towns as well as large cities. As John MacPhee previously explained that, for the greatest impact, it's important to apply the JED framework to all aspects of society.

On a national level, efforts are being made, but overall more needs to be done. Broad fragmentation of mental health care trickles down and negatively impacts communities. According to John MacPhee, serious infrastructure problems "only can be fixed when government wants to fix it." Until our government takes action, one way JED recommends we combat fragmentation is to mobilize communities.

Mobilizing communities means applying the JED model to structures outside of a school setting, including using the framework within cities. Several organizations have already embarked on this journey. One example is citiesRISE, which is an organization working with cities around the globe to bring mental health strategies to life.[105] In Seattle, local governments are working toward integrated delivery systems, allowing youth to lead. Nairobi is focused on developing mental health policies through working with local stakeholders. Bogotá is creating community-based models, partnering with the Secretary of Health.[106] These are just a few examples of how cities can and are using a comprehensive approach to suicide prevention.

Cities, companies, and communities can look to the JED framework and implement a comprehensive approach to suicide. As echoed throughout this book, suicide prevention needs to be on *everyone's* radar, not just colleges.

AMERICAN FOUNDATION FOR SUICIDE PREVENTION

OUT OF THE DARKNESS

Every year, thousands of people wearing colorful honor beads gather together and walk across their city to support suicide prevention. The American Foundation for Suicide Prevention (AFSP) is the largest private funder of suicide research in the world. AFSP is unique in blending research and advocacy

---

105 citiesRISE, "Local Collective Action."

106 Ibid.

together to enact change, with a mission to "save lives and bring hope to those affected by suicide."[107]

Robert Gebbia is the CEO of AFSP and helped to launch an initiative, Out of the Darkness Community Walks, to raise awareness and funding for suicide prevention. These walks take place in hundreds of cities every year, bringing together suicide loss survivors, people with lived experience, and those who support the cause. Walkers have the opportunity to wear honor beads that signify various connections to suicide. Each color of the beads signifies a loss:

- White—loss of a child
- Red—loss of a spouse or partner
- Gold—loss of a parent
- Orange—loss of a sibling
- Purple—loss of a relative
- Silver—loss of a first responder/military
- Green—a personal struggle or attempt
- Teal—supporting someone who struggles or has attempted
- Blue—supporting suicide prevention [108]

The Out of the Darkness Walk is a deep experience. As a junior in college doing this walk, I observed necklaces filled with a rainbow stream of colors, signifying each individual's connection to suicide, all united while fighting for the same cause.

---

107 American Foundation for Suicide Prevention, "About AFSP."

108 American Foundation for Suicide Prevention, "The Overnight Walk Honor Beads."

Robert Gebbia shared an inspiring memory of the first ever AFSP overnight walk that took place in 2002 at the nation's capital. Speaking to the crowd, he looked out at a sea of empowered people and realized in that moment that "every one of those people had a story, and every one of those people there were people that had lost someone...." Seeing all the families and the thousands impacted fuels him to do this work.

WE HAVE TO DO BETTER

Can you prevent every suicide? Robert Gebbia compared suicide to a heart attack. While it's not possible to prevent every heart attack, there are steps a person can take to minimize risk (e.g., avoid smoking, exercise, eat a nutritious diet, and limit alcohol).[109] For suicide prevention, there are also concrete steps, such as education on recognizing warning signs, and engaging people in open conversations.

Is suicide a preventable cause of death? For AFSP, the answer is yes—suicide is a preventable cause of death. Analogous to car accidents, they will inevitably happen, but there are things that can be done to reduce fatalities. He emphasizes, "We have to do better. We have to keep working," highlighting that there is a team of researchers, clinicians, and family members as a part of AFSP. On the collaboration between research and practice, he shared:

"Engagement of people together with the science, we think, is the formula to get something done here because you need

---

109 American Heart Association, "Lifestyle Changes."

people; you can't just be in the laboratory. On the other hand, you need the science, so you know the things that you are doing are the right things."

EVERYBODY'S BUSINESS

Robert Gebbia explains that colleges have a role to play, just like high schools do, in creating a culture that is open and in which students feel comfortable coming forward with concerns. But, again, responsibility isn't limited only to college campuses. The roles extend to any community, including faith organizations, the military, and workplaces. Nonprofits like AFSP are frequently based in large cities such as Washington, DC or New York City. However, suicide prevention work cannot only come from cities where many national organizations live. *Communities* need to have an active role as well. In his eyes, "Suicide is everybody's business because it has to be a community response."

Specifically on college campuses, Robert said that families should feel confident when sending kids to school, knowing that the school will be utilizing the best practices, including promotion of educational forums on mental health and suicide prevention, a culture in which it's OK to seek help, and available counseling services. If a school doesn't provide counseling services, there should be resources in place to refer a student off campus.

The foundation also believes that there should be availability of mental health screening for students. They created an interactive screening tool that connects students with counselors online for initial screening and treatment recommendations.[110] This is to combat the shame, fear, and self-stigma that so often prevent people from seeking help in-person. Through AFSP's Interactive Screening Program (ISP), students are able to anonymously connect with counselors from the counseling center without ever stepping foot into a building.

ACROSS STATE LINES

AFSP published a policy brief in 2019 outlining state laws in place for suicide prevention and mental health on college and university campuses.[111] Twelve of fifty states have laws in place, ranging in depth and content.

In New Jersey, the Madison Holleran Suicide Prevention Act requires a trained faculty to be reachable 24/7 and that students be made aware of contact information within fifteen days of each semester.[112]

In Indiana, public schools are required to develop and implement a suicide prevention policy, which includes:

1. crisis intervention access (e.g., hotlines)
2. mental health programs (e.g., teaching about suicide warning signs or available resources)
3. educational and outreach activities
4. support services (e.g., student organizations)

---

110 American Foundation for Suicide Prevention, "Interactive Screening Program."

111 American Foundation for Suicide Prevention, "AFSP State Laws."

112 Ibid.

5. postvention (e.g., strategic plan for how to communicate with community after loss by suicide)[113]

Texas requires institutions to provide mental health resources in a format that is not solely paper material handouts.[114] In California, institutions are required to print the national suicide prevention hotline number on all student IDs.

While progress has been made, thirty-eight states have no laws for suicide prevention on postsecondary higher education institutions. We could be doing better. The AFSP is working with states and other organizations, including JED, to provide recommendations for the best policies using evidenced-based frameworks.

---

113 Ibid.
114 Ibid.

CHAPTER 6:

CREATING HOPE THROUGH CONNECTEDNESS AND COMMUNITY

———

SUICIDE AWARENESS VOICES OF EDUCATION, EXECUTIVE DIRECTOR: DR. DANIEL REIDENBERG

Does the janitor working in the cafeteria have a role in preventing suicides on a college campus? What about the librarian in the computer science building? Or a student who notices that an acquaintance in their dorm has seemed a little disconnected recently? Should responsibility fall primarily on a college counseling center? Who is ultimately responsible for the role of suicide prevention on a college campus?

According to Dr. Daniel Reidenberg, executive director of Suicide Awareness Voices of Education (SAVE), *everyone* has a role in suicide prevention—whether or not you're on a college campus. This includes anyone from the faculty to resident assistants (RAs) to peers to administrators to those working in athletics to janitors to groundskeeping crews. Checking in with a student shouldn't be limited to only those who work in a counseling center. Dr. Reidenberg explained that "if [a groundskeeper] is taking care of the lawn, and they see someone who is very distressed, they should have just as much responsibility to go up to them and ask them how they are doing." He believes it is a problem in the field to say that only certain people have responsibility.

On why Dr. Reidenberg is motivated to do this work, he shared a powerful story:

"...A friend of mine, who I knew since I was one year old, died by suicide. Last time I saw him was on a college campus. We were in college together and I remember talking to him—this was more than twenty-five years ago now—and I remember where we were...on campus. And there was nothing back then. There was no place to go to. There was nothing to do. And nobody knew anything about the topic. Nobody wanted to talk about it. And just a couple days later, he died."

Now, thirty years later, we do know more about suicide on college campuses. There are counseling centers to go to, and people are talking more. We know that there is a comprehensive plan for approaching suicide. This includes awareness, policies, procedures, roles, responsibilities, programs, and trainings. Yet suicide rates have continuously increased. Clearly, more can be done.

He recommended all colleges should have the following to prevent suicide:

1. **Leadership** from the top and throughout
2. **Policies** that function to direct action and create accountability
3. **Services** that are available and accessible

Dr. Reidenberg stresses that the best way to see hope is through other people. There are various different ways to show hope to an individual who feels hopeless, whether this be through storytelling, being available, or seeing hope in what others are doing. His take-home message about why suicide prevention is important is there are people, there are resources, and there are treatments that work:

> "It doesn't have to end that way, it really doesn't...We have to find ways for people to see hope and believe in hope when they've lost it."

ACTIVE MINDS, CEO AND FOUNDER: ALISON MALMON
Alison Malmon was a college student when her older brother took his own life.

Soon after, in her dorm room, she started an organization that advocates for mental health initiatives on college campuses. A twenty-one-year-old undergraduate student, Alison realized the need for creating places on campus where students could discuss mental health. The mission of Active Minds is to inspire students to speak openly about mental health. Currently, there are over five hundred chapters of Active Minds across the nation that provide open spaces for students to discuss and advocate for mental health initiatives on their campuses.

Alison founded this organization in her brother's memory. She shared with me, "I need to think and talk about him, every single day...For suicide survivors, you just want people to say their name and remember the person that you lost and not think that they are gone forever."

As the CEO and founder of Active Minds, Alison has had students tell her that the organization saved their lives. Touched by these inspirational moments frequently, she said, "There is so much reason to have hope. I see it every day. That's what is pushing me to move forward."

Having the presence of Active Minds on campus has proven effective for students, whether or not they actively participated in the organization. A study published in the *Journal of the American Academy of Child and Adolescent Psychiatry* looked longitudinally at over 1,100 students across twelve California institutions.[115] The results reveal that increased familiarity with Active Minds was associated with increases

115   Active Minds, "Landmark Study."

in perceived knowledge of mental health, decreases in stigma, and increases in helping behaviors (e.g., connecting peers to services, providing emotional support). [116]

RESPONSIBILITY, STUDENT SUCCESS, AND CAMPUS CULTURE

Alison Malmon believes schools have a responsibility to permit and foster conversations about mental health. These conversations include openness and honesty not only from the counseling center, but also from professors and academic deans. She says this is imperative especially in times of exams and the week after orientation when "everything hits the fan."

Expanding on the topic of responsibility, one of the biggest challenges on college campuses is the issue of liability. She stated, "The moment we start talking about the responsibility of different entities, people tend to shy away and they become afraid." Responsibility may be implicitly associated with liability. However, shying away from these issues only further perpetuates mental health stigma. Fortunately, more people are opening up about mental health. As a result, institutions, companies, and professions have found themselves needing to confront issues that had previously been pushed aside.

Alison's perspective is that schools need to be addressing mental health as a key component of their students' overall success. If a student isn't emotionally healthy, they won't be a successful student. Alison suggests that one way to address student mental health could be assigning a mental health

---

116   Padilla et al., "Strengthening College Students.'"

adviser, just like an academic adviser, upon entry to the institution. Coming into school, each student will have different needs. She emphasizes, "Not all students on campus are students who are dealing with a diagnosed mental illness, but that still means that mental health is a core component of every student on campus."

We then discussed how the culture on many college campuses needs to shift. Alison says,

"It's an issue of culture. It's an issue of climate. It's not an issue of 'What's the one thing that we can do to fix this?' You need to change a culture in school. Colleges are representing what general society is. A lot of us experience this in high school or in the real world too. So it's not necessarily unique to colleges, but there's a unique opportunity for college campuses to do something about it. It's not easy."

GARDEN OF HOPE
SONG: "I BELIEVE"
ARTIST: CHRISTINA PERRI

The Active Minds chapter on my college campus ran a *Garden of Hope* exhibit for suicide and mental health awareness. Students woke up early in the morning to create a garden of 1,100 yellow pinwheels, lined with posters of hopeful messages.

Each year of college, the event had a distinct impact in my own life. On the day, I set my alarm early and met other students on the quad for set up. We spent a few hours before the sun rose, twisting each pinwheel into the dirt. Other students sat at a table for the day, offering local and national resources. People walking stopped to read the messages of inspiration and take a moment to pause.

Over the four years, I had reflections. Setting up the pinwheels my freshman year, mental health advocacy was a concept I had heard of before only faintly. By the time I was doing the same in my senior year, mental health advocacy was a huge piece of my life. Below are two posts from my social media, one from junior year and the next from senior year with some of my personal reflections of the *Garden of Hope*:

JUNIOR YEAR—FALL 2017

"This month is Suicide Prevention month. Suicide is the second leading cause of death among adolescents. Each year roughly 1,100 college students die by suicide. Every yellow pin wheel on the quad represents a student, with the intention of this day to bring awareness to suicide and prevention.

"For anyone going through a period of darkness, know that you are never alone. It is a really scary feeling to hit that low point. And it's easy to give up hope. But know that you are strong and you are beautiful. You do matter. And there is always a way to seek help."

—SEPTEMBER 22, 2017

SENIOR YEAR—FALL 2018

"This is my fourth year setting up pinwheels for suicide prevention week. Each year always brings up different feelings and emotions for me.

"I am still in the process of finding my peace. With senior year comes the expectation of having your life 'figured out.' There are additional pressures and the expectation that when someone asks you about the future, you have a plan. However, I can confidently say that I don't have my life 'figured out'...and I honestly don't think I ever will. I don't know where I will be in a year. And that is okay. It actually really excites me to know that the entire world is practically at my fingertips. I don't really want to have it all 'figured out' yet.

"That's not to say I don't have goals—I do. I eventually do want to pursue my PhD and continue to work in my passion of promoting community mental health and suicide prevention. But for right now, I have no idea where life will take me and that is okay :)

"...if you or a friend are currently experiencing suicidal ideation, please dial the National Suicide Prevention Lifeline at 1-800-273-8255. And remember that it's okay to not be okay. You are never alone."♥

—SEPTEMBER 14, 2018

As depicted in the photo of the garden from junior year, "Hope is the little voice that whispers 'maybe' when it seems the entire world is saying 'no.'" Events like the garden are meant to raise awareness, provide resources, and elicit hope. Thank you, Alison Malmon, for giving hundreds of students this space.

NATIONAL ALLIANCE ON MENTAL ILLNESS: JENNIFER ROTHMAN, SENIOR MANAGER OF YOUTH AND YOUNG ADULT PROGRAMS

Have you ever heard a description of someone's mental health story during a presentation that left you feeling confused? Discouraged? Disconnected? It's important for individual speakers to connect with their audience in a way that promotes overall mental health.

The National Alliance on Mental Illness (NAMI) works with people to train individuals with lived experience on how to tell their stories in a way that is not only informational, but also authentic and real, while being the least triggering possible.

NAMI is "dedicated to building better lives for the millions of Americans affected by mental health. As the largest grassroots' mental health organization in the country, [they] advocate for access to services and build communities of hope."[117] There are local affiliate chapters in communities across the country, with hundreds of individuals dedicated to raising awareness about mental illness. I had the opportunity to chat with Jennifer Rothman, the Senior Manager of Youth and Young Adult Initiatives for NAMI national.

A NEED FOR YOUNG PEOPLE

Jennifer shared with me that her inspiration for entering the field was fueled by childhood experiences with her mother, who was diagnosed with bipolar disorder. Periods of deep depression and electric shock therapy, were a lot for her family. This experience motivated her to go to school to study psychology in order to better understand what her mother was going through and help others.

When I asked her how she saw people with lived experience playing a role in the field, she specifically highlighted the need for more young people to be involved, stating:

"No matter how much we [older generations] love to think we are in touch with the younger population, we are not...The more we can invite young adults into the career, it will be better for all the young people who are affected. It brings new blood, new ideas."

Trends change quickly. Adolescents and young adults need people in the field who fully understand youth culture from

---

117   NAMI, "Frequently Asked Questions."

a first-person perspective. Jennifer Rothman's perspective is that one of the most important interventions a college can have is mandatory training for faculty and students at the start of every school year to remind students of what resources are available. In addition, she emphasized the importance of having staff members trained to recognize warning signs. Her biggest concern is the suicide rate for eighteen- to twenty-five-year-olds and even younger. She shared, "We are just not getting to them fast enough."

STORY SHARING

Hundreds of people share their stories in various communities around the country. There are many opportunities for college students to become involved in NAMI through any of the following avenues:

"NAMI Ending the Silence is a presentation designed for middle and high school students, school staff, and parents or guardians of middle or high school aged youth. Audiences learn about the signs and symptoms of mental health conditions, how to recognize the early warning signs, and the importance of acknowledging those warning signs."[118]

"NAMI Compartiendo Esperanza is a bilingual presentation for Latino communities designed to promote mental health awareness, explore signs and symptoms of mental health conditions, and highlight how and where to find help."[119]

---

118 NAMI, "Share Your Story."
119 Ibid.

"NAMI Sharing Hope is a presentation for African American communities designed to promote mental health awareness, explore signs and symptoms of mental health condition,s and highlight how and where to find help."[120]

"NAMI Smarts for Advocacy is a hands-on advocacy training program that helps people living with mental illness, friends, and family transform their passion and lived experience into skillful grassroots advocacy."[121]

"NAMI In Our Own Voice is a presentation for the general public to promote awareness of mental health conditions and recovery."[122]

Recalling a NAMI In Our Own Voice presentation, Jennifer remembered one specific story that stood out to her, given by a woman who had a prior suicide attempt. As a result of this attempt, first responders had been called who traveled with her to the hospital. While she was speaking to the crowd, she recognized the first responders who had traveled with her on the day of her attempt. At the end of her presentation, they came up to her and told her that they thought she had died that day. The reality was that this woman was not only alive, but was promoting help-seeking for others by sharing her personal experiences. The woman and the first responders ended up forming a friendship that has lasted to this day.

---

120 Ibid.
121 Ibid.
122 Ibid.

Colleges have the opportunity to invite presenters to campus and students are able to become involved in local chapters. After speaking with Jennifer, it seems even more apparent that colleges have the opportunity to successfully impact the mental health of their students by connecting with local NAMI chapters.

CHAPTER 7:

A PUBLIC HEALTH PERSPECTIVE

THE NATIONAL ACTION ALLIANCE FOR SUICIDE PREVENTION: DR. CAROLYN CLANCY

SONG: "ONE DAY"

ARTIST: MATISYAHU

Deaths of despair is a medical term used to describe the thousands of lives that are being lost each year to suicide and overdose. Dr. Carolyn Clancy prefers *deaths of disconnection,* which she feels more accurately reflects the feelings of isolation and disconnection that can lead to suicide.

Dr. Carolyn Clancy was recently recognized as one of the top fifty most influential clinical executives in the nation. She is the Codirector of the National Action Alliance for Suicide Prevention (NAASP) and Deputy Undersecretary of the Veterans Health Administration (VHA). Before leading the United States' main alliance for suicide prevention, she spent ten years as Director of the Agency for Healthcare Research and Quality (AHRQ).

SUICIDE PREVENTION: AMERICA'S PRIORITIES

NAASP is the country's leading alliance for suicide prevention. The US Surgeon General and the NAASP released a National Strategy for Suicide Prevention, which focuses primarily on transforming health systems, communities, and conversation. There are over 250 public and private partnerships that make up NAASP.

On the national level, these are the goals prioritized for suicide prevention in 2020:

1. *Integrate and coordinate suicide prevention activities across multiple sectors and settings.*
2. *Implement research-informed communication efforts designed to prevent suicide by changing knowledge, attitudes, and behaviors.*
3. *Increase knowledge of the factors that offer protection from suicidal behaviors and that promote wellness and recovery.*
4. *Promote responsible media reporting of suicide, accurate portrayals of suicide and mental illnesses in the entertainment industry, and the safety of online content related to suicide.*
5. *Develop, implement, and monitor effective programs that promote wellness and prevent suicide and related behaviors.*
6. *Promote efforts to reduce access to lethal means of suicide among individuals with identified suicide risk.*
7. *Provide training to community and clinical service providers on the prevention of suicide and related behaviors.*

8. *Promote suicide prevention as a core component of health care services.*

9. *Promote and implement effective clinical and professional practices for assessing and treating those identified as being at risk for suicidal behaviors.*

10. *Provide care and support to individuals affected by suicide deaths and attempts to promote healing, and implement community strategies to help prevent further suicides.*

11. *Increase the timeliness and usefulness of national surveillance systems relevant to suicide prevention and improve the ability to collect, analyze, and use this information for action.*

12. *Promote and support research on suicide prevention.*

13. *Evaluate the impact and effectiveness of suicide prevention interventions and systems, and synthesize and disseminate findings.*[123]

Many occupations are working together to figure out how to learn from one another and achieve these goals. Despite increases in collaboration, there remains a challenge: how do you reach people at an earlier stage—before a crisis arrives?

RESPONSIBILITY AND FIRST RESPONDERS

Surrounding many suicides is the response: "*I had no idea. I would have done something. What should I have done?*" says Dr. Clancy. But in her eyes, the only mistake you can make is to remain silent by not talking about suicide as a public health problem.

---

123 National Action Alliance for Suicide Prevention, "Goals and Objectives."

On the topic of who is responsible (cities, towns, or colleges, etc.) for preventing suicide, Dr. Clancy shared,

"I think everyone has a responsibility. Now, saying that almost absolves everyone in the same breath. So I think the practical answer is that we have to work together to figure out: how do we begin to make a dent in this big problem?"

Where Carolyn Clancy works, at VHA, she expresses that the challenge is even greater:

"Certainly, from the healthcare side, there remains a huge stigma about getting help for mental health problems. Any breathing person would say, of course, there's no stigma—and, of course, there is. People worry that it will affect their job, their livelihood, what other people think about them, and so forth."

Really take a moment to pause and think about her words. Awareness and anti-stigma campaigns have amplified in recent years, yet stigma is still pervasive. Suicide rates are still rising. And there is no simple answer as to why. It is a huge issue not only for universities, but also in the workplace—especially on the front lines.

Paramedics, firefighters, and police are often the first people there in the midst of a suicide crisis. Dr. Clancy recounted a time when she gave a talk to a room of first responders at a hospital. She reflected on that moment:

"...I said to them, if at some point when you're dealing with someone who is very, very seriously, considering [suicide], if you're not scared, you've missed something...I could almost

feel the room exhale, because it is scary. But that doesn't give us a right to back off and not do it."

In one study of over seven thousand firefighters, 65 percent of the people surveyed were "haunted by traumatic work situations." Yet more than 80 percent of the same sample said that reaching out for help would make them seem "weak or unfit for duty."[124] Walking into someone else's suicide attempt is a traumatic experience. First responders do this every single day.

On a college campus, the first to respond to a student in crisis ranges from student Resident Advisors to student EMS workers. We need to be doing a better job not just nationally, but also on college campuses to provide support, training, and resources and promote help-seeking among the individuals who play a crucial role in suicide intervention.

Talking with Dr. Clancy, I learned a lot and am encouraged by all that is being done on the national level. In creating campus-wide suicide prevention strategies, college administrators would do well to learn from the NAASP.

AMERICAN ASSOCIATION OF SUICIDOLOGY: AMY KULP

A BRIEF HISTORY

In the early nineties, suicide was only on the radar of few national and grassroots advocacy organizations. The pioneering of the suicide prevention movement stemmed from a

---

124 Suicide Prevention Resource Center, "Nation Data Shows Firefighters.'"

conference held in Reno, Nevada.[125] The conference brought together both private and public perspectives and produced eighty-one recommendations for the country. In 1999, as result of findings from the conference, US Surgeon General David Satcher released the "Surgeon General's Call to Action to Prevent Suicide," raising suicide as a public health concern. In a report from the CDC, he states:

"The nation must address suicide as a significant public health problem and put into place national strategies to prevent the loss of life and the suffering suicide causes...We must act now. We cannot change the past, but together we can shape a different future."[126]

Founded in 1968, one of the first national suicide prevention organizations, the American Association of Suicidology (AAS), *"envisions a world where people know how to prevent suicide and find hope and healing."*[127]

LISTEN TO SURVIVORS

I had the privilege of speaking with Amy Kulp, who has worked with AAS since 1995. As the Chief Operating Officer of AAS and the Director of the National Center for the Prevention of Youth Suicide, she has seen the field transform in the past thirty years. There is increased public and private partnerships and more knowledge about suicide prevention. However, she points out that for the needle to move toward

---

125   National Action Alliance for Suicide Prevention, "2012 National Strategy."

126   Ibid.

127   American Association for Suicidology, "About AAS."

truly reducing the number of youth suicides, there must be more increases in collaboration and the founding of one central umbrella organization or place that all people (loss survivors, clinicians, researchers, etc.) can turn to. Currently that does not exist because collaboration is something that doesn't necessarily come naturally. It requires energy to step outside one silo, and into another, and truly be able to learn from one another.

Amy Kulp stated, *"There are many more voices out there than are being heard,"* while highlighting the importance of coming together. Suicide attempt survivors and loss survivors offer a unique perspective in sharing what has been effective for coping mechanisms, recovery, and healing. Unfortunately, these voices were pushed out of research conferences and the field of suicide prevention for a long time. In 2014, AAS took the step to include the survivor voices that are "central to research, policy-making, public messaging, treatment, and support."[128]

On college campuses specifically, Amy Kulp emphasized the importance of:

1. Policies that are student-friendly and informed by research
2. Counselors that are trained in assessing and evaluating suicidal risk
3. Administration who is supportive of a campus-wide suicide prevention program

---

128 American Association for Suicidology, "Suicide Attempt Survivors."

Amy Kulp described her work as challenging and invigorating—specifically when seeing her personal and professional lives converge. She shared one such moment when a friend of her teenage daughter was struggling with sexual identities issues, not accepted by his family, and texted that he sometimes felt like he no longer wanted to live. She said that her teenage daughter knew how to respond to the text and "be there" as a result of growing up informed about suicide prevention and mental health. However, not all teenagers are aware of what to do in this situation. Suicide prevention is not always seen as a public health issue, therefore funding for psychoeducation is lacking. Amy Kulp says that suicide prevention doesn't necessarily have the same appeal for funding as other public health initiatives.

Public health campaigns have tackled drinking and driving, smoking cessation, and seatbelt use. As a result, accidents and fatalities have dropped. According to Amy Kulp, we *need* to be viewing suicide prevention from a similar public health perspective, which includes getting the funding to talk about suicide prevention in schools and to create awareness campaigns. We need to be doing more to view suicide prevention in the United States as a public health problem.

CHAPTER 8:

A SOCIAL JUSTICE PERSPECTIVE

———

SONG: "WHERE IS THE LOVE?"

ARTIST: BLACK EYED PEAS

In the "A Student Perspective" section, I spoke about a woman with a suicide plan whom I crossed paths with during my junior year. She will forever stand out in my mind. She shared her perspective that mental health is not recognized as "real" in the Black community and talked about how mental health issues are handled by placing people in prison, rather than through supportive services. Her words left their mark on me:

"You can't totally understand, but you are in a position where you can do something about it. I really hope you will make a difference in this field."

On the night we met, this woman had thanked me for helping her. In actuality, though, she was the one who had a huge impact on me. Her words and her experiences really stuck with me. She almost attempted suicide as a result of not having access to quality mental health services after being released from prison. She inspired me to reflect on mental health issues through another lens, the social justice lens: considering *all* the factors that really contribute to someone's story.

Systematic racism and mental health disparities are deeply linked (e.g., lack of access to care, dealing with mental health issues in the criminal justice system rather than through supportive services, cultural biases from health providers, and misdiagnoses such as attributing behaviors to delinquency as opposed to survival coping strategies for trauma).[129] I will never know how it feels to be negatively impacted by the systematic racism that exists in our country, but I do know that I can use my voice to say something about it. We need to do better. Our health care system *needs* to put energy toward addressing socioeconomic disparities in communities of color. I recognize that I am barely touching the surface of such an important topic. Entire books are dedicated solely to the impact of social justice issues on mental health. But it's important to introduce because when discussing college student mental health and suicide prevention, it is important to highlight the social justice issues that may contribute to a student's overall well-being.

---

129 Herman, "How Racism, Trauma, and Mental Health"

You can look at the numbers and statistics all day long and rationally conclude from the pages and pages of data that there is a problem in our country. But sometimes focusing too much on the numbers inadvertently removes the feelings associated with the numbers. How often do you ever really step back and think about what numbers mean? Behind every single data point in a statistical analysis, there is a story. Behind the 800, 000 people in the world who die by suicide each year, there is a story. Behind the 1.4 million people in the United States who attempt suicide each year, there is a story. Behind every person who experiences suicidal ideation, there is a story.

BROADER THAN THE MEDICAL MODEL

"Racism. Poverty. Injustice. Violence. Inequality. Discrimination. Socioeconomic status. Neglect. Trauma. Mass incarceration. Access to housing and healthcare. Food insecurity. Adverse Childhood Experiences (ACES). Sexism. Xenophobia. Transphobia. Homophobia. Assault. Oppression. Anti-Semitism. Unsafe home environments. Isolation. Police brutality. Lack of resources."[130]

The above factors are pulled from an online artwork piece and give additional context and "the stories" behind many of the datapoints. A local chapter of NAMI posted the image with the above items, a shovel, and the heading, "If we want to address mental health, we need to dig deeper."[131] This work speaks to the fact that addressing mental health must

---

130   Ruriani, "Dig Deeper Prints"

131   Ibid.

also include addressing social justice issues, with diverse intersectional elements. You cannot just look at a person's symptoms; you need to look at the broader picture. You need to acknowledge the injustices in our society. And you need to advocate for this to change.

IT'S REAL

Each college student has a story. It's important to acknowledge that those stories may include adverse childhood events, poverty, violence, racism, food insecurity, and more. One of my close friends from college described that while growing up, he never walked outside past sundown: it would have been dangerous because of gang violence. Freshman orientation week was the first time in his life that he walked outside at night—*ever*. Sophomore year of college, when he began experiencing symptoms of a mental health disorder related to traumatic experiences as a teenager, I expressed my concern and asked if he would be open to counseling. He laughed, referenced the community in which he grew up, and said, "Em—we don't do that." Eventually, his symptoms became severe enough that after some additional conversations, he realized that he needed to go to our counseling center. A couple years later, he thanked me, and told me that going to treatment saved his life.

This story is just one of many that illustrates that not everyone enters college with an education about mental health issues or comes from a supportive community or family. Students come to college with very different experiences. Some students come from very supportive home environments. For others, college is the first time there is a break from the storm. As I have mentioned, colleges have an opportunity to foster a culture where all students can begin to recognize mental health as *real* regardless of their home environment.

AFSP has a university resource related to this exact issue called *It's Real*. This documentary provides a diversity of individual student accounts. One college student states,

"...You don't have to be a completely new person just because you go to college...The things and the baggage that you had in high school, they might come with you to college. And that's totally okay...You don't have to be the perfect person."[132]

This documentary is just one example of how a school can begin to foster open conversations about mental health issues. Colleges have an opportunity to talk openly about intersectional additional contextual factors of mental health—factors that go beyond symptoms and data points.

MENTAL HEALTH AMERICA: KELLY DAVIS, DIRECTOR OF PEER ADVOCACY, SUPPORT, AND SERVICES

"Feeling like we must fix what our friends share can keep us from doing the most important thing, which is often just being there," wrote Kelly Davis wrote in an article detailing how to help a friend who is struggling with their mental health.[133]

Kelly, a dedicated mental health advocate for college students, is the Director of Peer Advocacy, Support, and Services for

---

132 American Foundation for Suicide Prevention, "It's Real."

133 Davis, "How Can I Help a Friend."

Mental Health America (MHA). This organization is a leading nonprofit with the mission to address the needs of those living with mental illness, and to promote the overall mental health of all Americans.[134]

Mental Health America published a position statement in March 2019 on how colleges and universities can respond to the student mental health crisis. Its call to action included four key items:

1. Colleges and universities should provide a variety of mental health resources to proactively reach students where they are.
2. College and university policies should prevent students with mental health conditions from experiencing stigma and discrimination.
3. Colleges and universities should develop protocols to respond fairly and effectively to students in crisis.
4. Policies should limit liability for colleges and universities to encourage proper protocols.[135]

INCLUDE THE STUDENT PERSPECTIVE

At its core, in the eyes of Kelly Davis, mental health equity is a social justice and civil rights issue. In any type of social justice work, the people who are most impacted are the ones at the forefront leading the change. In the case of college student mental health, this means college students themselves are leaders. Colleges have a responsibility to work with

---

134   Mental Health America, "About."

135   Mental Health America, "Position Statement."

student leaders to address whatever issues are most pressing, including student mental health and well-being.

However, we know that many times administrators are creating policies and making decisions about student mental health without including the student perspective. Kelly points out that *"the people who are in positions of power right now who are making these decisions grew up in a world that is radically different than what is happening now."*

She highlights the fact that there are distinct stressors that affect young people differently today than decades ago, when many people in administrative roles were either in college or had received training. For example, many more students now are coming to college already prescribed psychiatric medication or having gone through therapy. While there are many rising issues, there are also solutions, one being clear: include young people as leaders.

MODELS OF DISABILITY

The heart and soul of Kelly's work is driven in part by her lived experiences. She is very open about having been given thirteen different psychiatric diagnoses and, at the same time, is very open to critiquing the field of mental health. Her work has centered around explicitly naming what is insufficient in the field and coming up with alternatives: an hour a week of therapy and a psychiatrist can be helpful to some, but they aren't a universal panacea. Individual-focused interventions aren't enough to create a fully inclusive environment for students with psychiatric disabilities.

Her program at MHA, the Collegiate Mental Health Innovation Council (CMHIC), is dedicated to finding and expanding student-led and developed programs that fill gaps in traditional services and supports on campuses. Providing examples of alternatives to one-on-one counseling, Kelly suggests adding peer support programs, creating avenues where students feel comfortable discussing their lived experiences, increasing supportive communities in which students can actively learn skills, and creating a well-being course for students.

Mental health work expanding from the individual-level to the cultural-level is needed in order to adequately address the root of college mental health concerns. The medical model of disability defines disability as "a medical phenomenon that results in impairments from body functions or structures; a deficiency or abnormality."[136] In this model, a person with a mental health disability would be seen as a problem that needs to be cured. The disability is perceived as fundamentally negative. In contrast, the social model of disability defines disability as "a social construct that is imposed on top of impairments by society; a difference."[137] In this model, barriers exist in society that prohibit a person with disabilities from being on the same playing field in a culture that is not necessarily inclusive. The person with a disability is seen as neither positive or negative. This model is relevant for mental health conditions—looking just at the medical model is not always sufficient.

---

136 Haegel, "Disability Discourse," 195.

137 Ibid.

Colleges have an opportunity to be at the forefront of shifting this culture and destigmatizing mental health conditions.

DR. ROSIE PHILLIPS DAVIS

SONG: "I AM LIGHT"

ARTIST: INDIA.ARIE

Take a moment to think of yourself outside of any external labels: outside of the money in your bank account, who are you? Outside of the GPA on your transcript or the employment positions listed on your resume, who are you? Outside of your social media and online presence, who are you? Outside of the way you think you should be, who are you? What in your life gives you meaning?

In our interview, Dr. Davis, the 2019 president of the American Psychological Association (APA), says:

"It's amazing how humans don't change. People need to have a sense of connection. A sense of belonging. They need to be affirmed. That doesn't change no matter what your station is in life. No matter how much training you have or how many degrees you have."

Erasing the labels, she touches on a component that is essential for *everyone's* well-being: human connection.

DEEP POVERTY INITIATIVE

Throughout her time with the APA, Dr. Davis's work incorporated this understanding, primarily focusing on a deep poverty initiative. The APA is the leading scientific and professional organization of psychology in the United States. Below are three areas she focused on as president:

1. *Collaborated with experts in the psychological science of poverty to better understand the structural links between poverty and behavioral, mental, and physical health challenges.*
2. *Raised awareness among key stakeholders—Congress, corporations, and communities—of what psychological science tells us about deep poverty and attitudes toward those living in deep poverty.*
3. *Elevated the role of psychology in addressing societal issues rooted in poverty by reshaping the narrative surrounding it and the policies that contribute to it.*[138]

Dr. Davis and I discussed how common it is in our society to attach "us" versus "them" labels to people, when the reality is that at the end of the day, we are *all* people.

"We talk a lot about walking in somebody else's shoes, but it's a very difficult thing to do, especially if somebody has shoes with holes in them. You don't even want to put them on,"

DR. ROSIE PHILLIPS DAVIS SAID.

---

138 American Psychological Association, "APA President."

I listened as she told me a story about one of the students on her campus. Walking around campus in a suit with a stellar GPA, this student always appeared put-together. It wasn't until the end of his senior year that he disclosed the reality of his situation: he was homeless. Sleeping on floors with lots of other people, he had nowhere to go. Dr. Davis stressed that poverty isn't always the person on the street. With over thirty years of experience working on college campuses, Dr. Davis has seen many students who are homeless or home insecure and who struggle with limited resources for food and other basic essential items.

Our society's socioeconomic disparities are mirrored on college campuses. College is expensive. Some students are under extreme financial stress, thousands of dollars in debt, needing to work multiple jobs to stay afloat, which in turn significantly impacts mental health. Financial stress has been seen to be "associated with suicide risk among college students."[139] In referring students to longer-term, private, off-campus treatment, college counseling centers need to consider that the high cost of treatment may be a barrier to many. Financial difficulties can also impact a student's ability to purchase housing, books, food, and supplies. It's important for colleges to recognize financial stress as a potential contributor to poor mental health and suicide risk.

RESPONSIBILITY: OBLIGATION TO CARE
On the role or responsibility of colleges, Dr. Davis shared that it would be in a given university's best interest to protect

---

139   HanNa, Lim. "Financial Stress Self-Efficacy, and Financial Help Seeking."

student mental health and prevent suicide because of success in retention. If colleges want students to donate back, don't want bad press, and seek higher graduation rates, it's in the best interest of those universities to care about student mental health. And from her perspective, colleges are obligated to care for their students.

She pointed out that working in higher education will not make you rich. Generally, people working in higher education don't want to see students hurting, and they are there because they want to "live a life with purpose." She stressed that it is important to get diverse voices all in one room in order to make the best decisions possible for students.

Dr. Davis ended the interview by saying,

"You're in a position where people really want to listen to you. Never underestimate your power. Remember to always give yourself a support team because somebody will tell you 'no', but 'no' means 'not right now.'"

Her message is one that can be taken to all young people. In advocacy work, people do say no. There are road bumps. It is hard work—but at the same time, it is work that needs to be done. Sometimes, as a young person, I know I have questioned the power of my own voice in the mix of people with impressive titles and degrees doing so much of this work.

However, what I know to be true is young people do have the power to enact change.

A POLITICIAN AND ADVOCATE PERSPECTIVE: FORMER CONGRESSMAN PATRICK J. KENNEDY

WE NEED A MOVEMENT

"Young people know how to make their voices heard...They just aren't doing it in this space...In recovery, you can't make someone recover. They have to want it."

—PATRICK J. KENNEDY

Young people have been at the forefront of social justice movements for the past century: the civil rights movement, the fight for gender equality, and the fight for rights for the LGBTQ+ community were all led in large part by younger voices. According to Kennedy, *"You can't orchestrate or manufacture a movement,"* and young people need to make their voices heard in the mental health world. There has yet to be a large public outcry, and until there is a sense of urgency to respond to the mental health crisis, change by legislative action will continue to be slow.

In 2013, Patrick J. Kennedy founded the Kennedy Forum, which aims *"to unite the health care system, and rally the mental health community around a common set of principles"* through:

- *Full implementation of federal and state parity laws*

- *Quality and transparency in mental health care*
- *Integration—ensuring mental health care is incorporated into our larger health care system*
- *Technology as a way to improve access to care and quality of care*
- *Brain health and fitness with a focus on early interventions and research*[140]

Before founding the Kennedy Forum, Patrick J. Kennedy served in the U.S. House of Representatives from 1995 to 2011 as a Democratic senator from Rhode Island. He is the son of Ted Kennedy, who served as a Massachusetts senator for nearly five decades, and the nephew of President John F. Kennedy.

In 2015, Patrick J. Kennedy coauthored the book *A Common Struggle: A Personal Journey Through the Past and Future of Mental Illness and Addiction*, which details his personal struggles, as well as his bold plan for the future of mental health care in America. In breaking his family's "code of silence," Kennedy openly challenged the stigma that often deters families from facing mental illness or addiction head-on.

MENTAL HEALTH PARITY

The last bill that President John F. Kennedy signed into law before his assassination was the Community Mental Health Act in 1963. At the time, mental illness was treated primarily in asylums, and the then-president envisioned bringing

---

140 The Kennedy Forum, "How We'll Do It."

those affected by mental illness to community-based centers instead.

Mental health wasn't then covered to the same extent as physical health. Decades later in 2008, Patrick Kennedy wrote the Mental Health Parity and Addiction Equity Act (Federal Parity Law), which requires insurers to cover treatment for mental health and substance use disorders no more restrictively than treatment for illnesses of the body, such as diabetes and cancer.[141]

Unfortunately, most insurance providers are still not fully compliant with the law because of a lack of enforcement, leading to huge out-of-pocket expenses for those seeking care for mental health or substance use disorders. Some families are forced to limit or forgo care altogether—a reality that has contributed to our nation's historic rates of overdoses and suicides.[142]

College mental health exists within a larger picture: the national health care system. In Patrick J. Kennedy's book, he highlights that our health care system often ignores *"treatment from the neck up,"* or in other words, brain health. The Kennedy Forum has a vision to change the way mental health care is delivered, in which the brain is looked at as equal to any other organ in the body.

To achieve that vision, it works to unite advocates, business leaders, and government agencies in support of

---

141 The Kennedy Forum, "Parity Progress."

142 Don't Deny Me, "Don't Be Denied: Equal Rights."

evidence-based practices, policies, and programming in mental health and addiction. Its most recent collaboration, the Don't Deny Me campaign, educates consumers and providers about patient rights under the Federal Parity Law, and connects them with essential appeals guidance and resources.[143]

BREAKING THE SILENCE

When I spoke with Patrick J. Kennedy, he said the most rewarding part of sharing his story has been increasing the number connections he has with people who personally identify, emphasizing that in recovery, these connections are essential to sobriety. He said that the most challenging piece of sharing his story has been deviating from the culture in which he was raised:

"The challenging part is breaking the family ethos, which says that it's best to be quiet and it's best to keep these things "private." And that's basically a way of saying it's best to be silent, and that's a kind of an attitude that sticks with you because it's from your family of origin. Anyone who has grown up in an alcoholic home knows that mantra. But they also know the only way to get into recovery and to break cycles of addiction and dysfunction and codependency is to call out what is unhealthy. The difficult part is doing that, just because it's not a familiar thing to act in a way that is contrary to how you've been brought up. But it's part of the growing process that you do in recovery."

---

143 Don't Deny Me, "Equal Access."

Speaking up in a family system or in a culture that does not support mental health is incredibly difficult. On college campuses, there are students entering from both supportive and unsupportive family backgrounds. Colleges have the opportunity to make speaking up about mental health easier for *all* entering students, whether they come from an environment where this was encouraged or discouraged.

In his book, Kennedy says: "*Organizations like the JED Foundation and Active Minds would be even more effective if the colleges and universities were more proactive...*" When I asked him to expand on what he meant by this, he explained a need for university leadership to make mental health a top priority. By bringing in all of the experts, a university can assess available community and campus resources, acknowledging both fall "*woefully short*" of meeting needs, and come up with additional ways to try to mitigate demand. He highlighted the importance of "upstream prevention" and building a compassionate community to combat feelings of isolation.

RALLYING ON COLLEGE CAMPUSES

Speaking with Patrick J. Kennedy, I felt inspired and empowered. Young people can take action to move the needle not only in shifting campus cultures, but also in advocating for additional resources and quality care. Mental health issues and addiction need to be viewed as *health* issues.

You read earlier about how some students feel punished or kicked off campus for experiencing a mental health crisis (e.g., suicide attempt, hospitalization). If you are someone or know someone with these experiences, I encourage you to speak up to administrators and share your student perspective. You have read that college counseling centers often have wait times to access care, limited sessions, and other problems. If you have been affected, I encourage you to speak up and share your perspective. You read that an estimated one in four students are affected by significant mental health issues during college. You read that college students, regardless of mental health issues, are affected by a culture that puts health on the backburner. Your voice holds more power than you think it does. There is strength in numbers—gather friends and classmates, and speak up. Mental health needs to be looked at in the same light as physical health. We need to start a movement.

CHAPTER 9:

RESEARCH, IMPLEMENTATION, AND DISSEMINATION

SONG: "SEND THEM OFF!"

ARTIST: BASTILLE

A NEUROSCIENTIST PERSPECTIVE: DR. THOMAS INSEL

"Our house is on fire and you're talking about the chemistry of the paint." This was spoken by a community member who stood up and addressed Dr. Thomas Insel at the end of his presentation.

In this moment, Dr. Insel paused. As one of the worldwide leading neuroscientists and the Director of the National Institute of Mental Health (NIMH), he was accustomed to sharing cutting-edge science. Yet this community member had a good point. While researchers at NIMH were celebrating advances in neuroscience, public health measures were not improving. Over the previous thirteen years while directing the NIMH, he shared with me that the mortality rate from suicide had increased 33 percent and the morbidity from schizophrenia hadn't decreased.

Dr. Insel reflected on the disconnect between science and implementation, and his thought-process around switching to the private technology sector:

"I don't want to spend another ten years funding spectacular science that has really no evident impact on ending the public health curb. If ten years from now, I'm still doing this, and the suicide rate had gone up yet another 33 percent, that would really be unacceptable. That would be egregious."

He emphasized the need for having both a long and short view. The deep research science that NIMH supports is *critical* in the long run to have a clearer understand of what is happening in the brain. At the same time, he shared that it is important to have a short-term plan as well because the public cannot wait twenty years to begin to see the suicide rate come down.

The gap between what we know and what we actually do needs to be closed by leadership in order for improvements to be seen. He shared, *"Why are we so focused on developing new medicines when so many people aren't getting the current medicines?"*

After the above-mentioned presentation on the West Coast in 2015, he was motivated to switch from the public sector to private tech to see if there would be a better way to put out the fire in a time frame that honors the urgency of the problem. After thirteen years of directing the NIMH, Dr. Thomas Insel joined Verily, a start-up emerging from Google's idea factory, Google X. Verily was formed to use Google's software expertise on health problems, from a closed-loop system for managing diabetes to new diagnostics for cancer. In the mental health space, Verily focused on digital phenotyping, a method for assessing mood and cognition passively from smartphones and wearables. After eighteen months at Verily, he cofounded Mindstrong Health to apply digital phenotyping in the health care system.[144] Mindstrong Health used smartphones to improve measurement through continuous, passive, ecological assessment with careful protection of privacy. Most recently, Dr. Insel has launched a new company, NEST Health. NEST stands for Network to Engage, Support, and Thrive. NEST was founded specifically to focus on digital care for college students, using teletherapy and creating a supportive community where members get and give help.

On a national level, he explained that mental health issues are being dealt with in many places outside of the health care system, including in the criminal justice system, schools, and homeless shelters. People often like to focus on access and stigma as the big problems surrounding mental health. However, he noted that addressing fragmentation and quality are extremely important as well. If people are getting access to treatment—but it is the wrong treatment—outcomes won't

144 Mindstrong, "Mental Health Care."

necessarily improve. He highlighted that the bar needs to be raised for standards of care. In providing care, it is crucial to use evidenced-based treatment. For medical conditions such as heart disease or diabetes, if a person were treated by non-evidenced-based interventions, the provider would lose their license. The same standard should apply to mental health treatment. Quality in providing care and raising the bar in standards of care are essential for improving mental health outcomes.

Research demonstrates that there are concrete actions that can be taken to reduce risk for suicide. We know that a person is most at risk for dying by suicide in the thirty days after a first suicide attempt. We know that about 50 percent of the time, when someone is discharged from the emergency room after a suicide attempt, no one follows up. According to Dr. Insel, *"Not only do we fail on prevention, but we fail on postvention."*

We know a lot about how to reduce suicide. Dr. Insel claims, *"You can't eradicate suicide, probably one of those parts of the human condition that are with us forever. But we can do a lot better, and we know that because [suicide rates] have not always been this high."* For suicide prevention specifically, there are many public health interventions that could be taken to reduce lethal means. This includes putting nets on nearby bridges, prohibiting firearms on campus, placing carbon dioxide detectors on campus cars, restricting access to the roofs of buildings, and monitoring or controlling access to toxic substances found in laboratories.[145]

---

145 Harvard T.H. Chan School of Public Health, "Means Matter."

It is imperative that leaders within colleges assess their own prevention, intervention, and postvention strategies to reduce suicide risk. They must look at what they can be doing on their campuses to implement measures that could reduce access to lethal means as well as improve quality of care.

A HEALTH ECONOMIC POLICY PERSPECTIVE: DR. DANIEL EISENBERG

"Rather than responsibility, what is the best use of resources, and what can colleges do most effectively?" Dr. Eisenberg responded when I asked him about his perspective on whether or not colleges are responsible for preventing suicide on their campuses. Dr. Eisenberg has a background in health policy, and relayed that it is often in the best overall interest of the college to reach people in distress and effectively refer them to resources.

Dr. Eisenberg is the director of the Healthy Minds Network (HMN), based at the University of Michigan. The HMN spans over three hundred institutions and involves a study that is sent out to college students across the nation. The Healthy Minds study is one of the only epidemiological studies used by institutions with a focus primarily on assessing mental health and treatment use of college students on their campus. The study screens categories of psychopathology, including anxiety, depression, disordered eating, and self-injurious thoughts and behaviors, painting a "detailed picture of mental health and related issues" on campuses.[146]

---

146 Eisenberg and Ketcher, "The Healthy Minds Study."

Dr. Eisenberg has seen the impact of the HMN from an aggregate level, as universities are able to advocate for more resources using the data collected. I personally relied on the Healthy Minds online calculator during my presentation to the board of trustees when describing the return on investment my college would save in proactively investing in student mental health and suicide prevention. Dr. Eisenberg shared that he was compelled to work in this area specifically because he could see the ways the HMN could have a positive impact on a wide scale.

He also described challenges faced with this type of research. For example, a practical challenge faced by any kind of population level online study is response rate, and as a result, potential response bias. The Healthy Minds survey is randomized to emails within a university, and roughly 25 percent of students who receive the email complete the Healthy Minds study. Dr Eisenberg stressed that the HMN works to address such challenges. In the 2019 study listed below, the HMN as able to address the response bias by constructing response weights of administrative data variables.[147]

These were the key findings from the 2019 study (seventy-nine schools; n =62,171 students):

- Thirty-six percent screened positive for major or moderate depression (PHQ-9).
- Thirty-one percent screened positive for anxiety (GAD-7).
- Ten percent screened positive for an eating disorder (SCOFF).

147 Ibid.

- Thirty-four percent screened positive for elevated eating concerns (CCAPS-34)
- Sixty-five percent engaged in binge drinking at least once in the past two weeks.
- Twenty-four percent engaged in non-suicidal self-injury (past year).
- Fourteen percent experienced suicidal ideation (past year).
- Forty percent of students screened positive for positive psychological well-being (note: the inverse of this means that 60% did not meet criteria for being psychologically healthy).
- Largest barrier to help-seeking: "No need for services" (41%).
- Public stigma item: "I would think less of someone who has received mental health treatment" (6%).
- Perceived stigma item: "Most people would think less of someone who has received mental health treatment" (47%).[148]

The data gained from such studies in invaluable. Taking a moment to reflect on the results: 60 percent of students did not meet criteria for being psychologically healthy. More students perceived stigma to be present than endorsed public stigma themselves. Roughly a fourth of students engaged in non-suicidal self-injury within the past year. And rates of anxiety and depression were both around a third of the sample. It is thus imperative that colleges work toward increasing awareness and access to services. Campus-wide studies allow for colleges to get a better sense of the symptomatology of students on campus in order to "identify needs and

---

148 Ibid.

priorities, benchmark against other peer institutions, evaluate programs and policies, plan for services and programs, and advocate for additional resources."[149]

A STATISTICIAN PERSPECTIVE: DR. BETH ANN GRIFFIN, SENIOR STATISTICIAN, RAND CORPORATION

Dissemination is absolutely imperative for the Research and Development (RAND) Corporation, an organization that leads in public health and public policy research. I had the opportunity to speak with Dr. Beth Ann Griffin, senior statistician at the RAND Corporation, who shared her insights on the importance of using the best statistical methods for research. Dr. Griffin was inspired to go into the field of public health because she wanted to make sure that her work had an application-grounded impact. She shared:

"As a statistician, my goal is to ensure that the research is actually robust and that the findings are accurate...That's...my day-to-day obsession...looking at whatever data set I'm working on and making sure we're doing the right analyses."

Dr. Griffin works with one of the largest databases for adolescents in treatment for substance use in the United States. She has examined which treatment programs are most effective for adolescent substance users, and developed methodologies with colleagues for how to analyze observational data in a robust way. RAND has a fundamental desire to make sure its findings get out to the public (excluding classified research).

---

149 Ibid.

Dr. Griffin is also a coinvestigator on Gun Policy in America, which is an initiative to understand the effects of gun policies and violence. Funded in part by the Arnold Ventures, her team analyzed thousands of studies in order to see if gun policies had an impact on outcomes, including suicide. Strong evidence supports that child access prevention (CAP) laws have an effect on decreasing suicide rates.[150] CAP laws allow for charges to be made against adults who carelessly allow children to be unsupervised with guns.[151] Yet 46 percent of states do not have these laws in place.[152]

Their work showed a 0.97 probability that a CAP law is associated with a decline in firearms deaths. The estimated effect size represents a decline of 6 percent (IRR=0.94) of the expected firearm death rate without the law. This effect size corresponds to 2,536 (80 percent CI 783 to 4,324) fewer firearm deaths nationally in 2016 if CAP laws had been implemented in all states beginning in 2010 relative to having been implemented in no states. In terms of firearm suicides, their work showed an estimated effect size of CAP laws on firearm suicides that represents a decline of 5 percent (IRR = 0.95) of the expected firearm suicides without the law. This effect size corresponds to 1,075 (80 percent CI 17 to 2,163) fewer firearm suicides nationally in 2016 if CAP laws had been implemented in all states beginning in 2010 relative to having been implemented in no states. Sensitivity analyses showed similar or even larger reductions in firearm suicides due to CAP laws among minors.

150   RAND, "How Gun Policies."

151   RAND, "The Effects of Child-Access Prevention Laws."

152   RAND, "How Gun Policies."

In addition, moderate evidence was found for waiting periods on suicide rates. There was also some evidence to suggest that licensing and permitting requirements, as well as minimum age requirements, may have an effect on decreasing rates of suicide. After the Parkland, Florida, shooting in 2018, RAND saw a surge in teenage users visiting their website. In the midst of tragic events, people were looking for accurate information about gun policy research. While RAND offers open access to their research, unfortunately, many organizations do not.

Unfortunately, as Dr. Griffin noted, there is too often a lengthy lag in the research world between findings being published in peer-reviewed, academic journals and them being disseminated and implemented in the real world. Evidence-based suicide prevention and college mental health programs don't get adopted in a timely enough fashion for students.

CHAPTER 10:

FROM THE FRONT LINES: COUNSELING CENTER DIRECTORS

SONG: "PUT DOWN WHAT YOU ARE CARRYING"

ARTIST: TREVOR HALL AND BRETT DENNEN

College counseling centers and the staff are the ones working on the ground, interacting with students in crisis on a daily basis. They're the ones seeing the direct impact of the demand crisis: students who arrive frustrated with long waiting lists, universities that expect them to be a fix-all solution, and fellow staff who are often burnt out by rising caseloads.

Do you believe colleges are responsible for 1) preventing suicide or 2) promoting mental health?

I reached out to counseling center directors for an answer to these and other questions. In the following interviews, directors reflect on what motivated them to start working with students. They touch on the challenges faced in addressing both mental health and suicide on their campuses. And they give hope for the future of mental health promotion and suicide prevention.

DR. BENJAMIN LOCKE (PENN STATE UNIVERSITY)

From a table in the back of the auditorium on Penn State University's campus, I jotted down notes using the pen distributed at the beginning of the Higher Education Suicide Prevention Coalition (HESPC) Conference:

"It's *not* a college student mental health crisis...," I scribbled down.

Then I realized what I had just written on the page.

Huh? Not a mental health crisis? As a junior in college, my eyebrows raised. But I continued to listen. I was curious.

Dr. Benjamin Locke then presented a decade of data that reflected the crisis wasn't limited to just colleges. And, to him, the larger crisis itself on college campuses was actually not a mental health crisis. Rather, the biggest "crisis" is in demand. More students are presenting to the counseling centers than ever before. Counseling centers are struggling to keep up. I wanted to learn more, so I reached out to Dr. Locke, who graciously agreed to be interviewed for this book.

Dr. Benjamin Locke is the senior director of Penn State's Counseling and Psychological Services and the executive director of the Center for Collegiate Mental Health (CCMH).

Collecting data from hundreds of counseling centers across the country, CCMH is a leading center focused on dissemination and implementation research for systematic changes.

In our interview, Dr. Locke shared that when he first began his work and over the course of a few years, he saw a "massive change" in the demand of students entering into the counseling center. At the time, he was concerned that policy decisions were being made by opinions rather than driven by data. That is what led him to "think about starting a center for collegiate mental health, to bring the voices of students, treatment, and also the clinicians who are treating them back into focus." He echoed a common theme: "numbers impact policy."

The 2019 annual report of the CCMH includes deidentified data from 207, 818 unique college students at 163 universities; these were all individuals who received mental health services (i.e., not the general population).[153] Highlights from the report include:

- Top ten concerns of students presenting to counseling centers as rated by clinicians:

  1. Anxiety
  2. Depression
  3. Relationship problem (specific)
  4. Stress
  5. Family
  6. Trauma

---

153   Center for Collegiate Mental Health, "2019 Annual Report," 5.

7. Grief/loss
8. Interpersonal Functioning
9. Adjusting to new environment
10. Academic performance

- Almost forty percent of all treatment-seeking students reported some suicidal ideation within the past two weeks[154]

- Self-reported anxiety and depression have increased over the past eight years. Trauma increased in the past six years. Academic distress, hostility, and substance use have remained flat or slightly decreased over the past several years.[155]

- For students presenting to the counseling center, 21.8 percent had attended counseling prior to college and 8.8 percent had taken a prescribed medication for mental health concerns prior to starting college.[156]

- Twenty-five percent of students checked that they had experienced the following: sexual contact "without your consent (e.g., you were afraid to stop what was happening, passed out, drugged, drunk, incapacitated, asleep, threatened or physically force)."[157]

---

154 Center for Collegiate Mental Health, "2019 Annual Report," 13.

155 Ibid.

156 Center for Collegiate Mental Health, "2019 Annual Report," 27.

157 Center for Collegiate Mental Health, "2019 Annual Report," 28.

- And 41.4 percent of students checked that they had experienced "a traumatic event that caused you to experience intense fear, helplessness, or horror." Of those students, the most commonly selected traumatic events were:

1. Childhood emotional abuse
2. Sexual violence
3. Other
4. Childhood physical abuse
5. Childhood sexual abuse[158]

These are the students presenting to college counseling centers across the nation. The statistics speak for themselves. Many college counseling centers aren't set up to provide more than a few sessions. The reality is that many of these students need longer-term treatment, especially for trauma.

Whether or not an institution is responsible for providing mental health treatment is an active debate in the field. How much health care or mental health treatment should a university provide? What services should be paid for by the student or family, versus the school? What if students need long-term care? What if a student is hospitalized? Is that the institution's responsibility or the student's?

Dr. Ben Locke shared his opinion that short-term counseling (e.g., crisis services, stabilization, and safety planning) needs to be viewed as a public health concern. It is in everyone's

_____

158 Ibid.

best interest to make these available to students without fees. He noted:

"The capacity of the counseling center is determined by the institution...One of the pieces that has been missed historically is that folks look at mental health services in higher education and they say, 'Well, the counseling centers aren't doing enough...,' And that's never the case...What's happening is that the counseling center's funding is not sufficient of matching a perceived need."

Blame commonly falls on the counseling centers, when the reality is that these centers are trying the best that they can, given the resources that the institution allocates. Dr. Ben Locke believes that if institutions of education (kindergarten through twelfth grade and higher education) care about students, then "they are charged with responsibility for investing time, money, energy" for preventing suicide (e.g., teach warning signs, engage with people at elevated risk, refer students).

Many universities benefit financially from student success (i.e., sports, career, education). Because institutions benefit directly from their students, institutions "should take responsibility for helping to manage the fallout that can go along with that." He believes colleges and universities have a responsibility to have programming in place that builds a supportive, caring, and attentive community in order to "do everything they can to prevent suicide on campuses."

IT STARTS IN ELEMENTARY SCHOOL

According to Dr. Locke, Shifting a culture starts in elementary school. He said that pursuit of higher education often falls into a continuum: some students are the first in their family to go to college, for others college is the next expected step, and a large percentage of all students have been "coping with high levels of academic pressures since the earliest years of school." By the time students get to college, many have been coping with an extreme amount of pressure that colleges continue to contribute to.

According to Dr. Locke, mental health issues are very much related to academic pressures, especially at highly competitive colleges. Competitive colleges consistently expect high standards, market themselves as successful top-notch institutions, and make it clear to all that being competitive is a major priority. Changing a culture isn't easy, but Dr. Locke emphasized that it can start with institutions approaching students with a "note of encouragement to take a deep breath and say, 'This is all going to work out.'" There need to be mechanisms in place for students to take a break; they need to know it's okay to change paths, rather than have an "all or nothing" mentality around their future. He elaborated that highly selective schools need to "invest a real energy into changing the culture around all or nothing performance," especially when students arrive from a pressure cooker educational system they've been in since elementary school.

WHY COLLEGE STUDENTS?

Dr. Locke was drawn to working with college students specifically because, in his eyes, these students are often highly motivated. For him, there is a sense of hopefulness that change could really happen. He has seen this change as a clinician on the individual level. From a psychologist's perspective, he shared with me that the most rewarding part of his job is sitting down with students in distress—who are feeling "at the end of their rope"—and then seeing positive changes over a fairly short period of time. He has helped students "find new pathways, new solutions, new ways of managing or coping" and later has seen students come back smiling a month or two later with a sense of "okay, this is all going to work out."

On a systemic level, he has seen the years of work with CCMH gathering data directly impact policy at the highest tiers. At a conference with university presidents, one cited the work being done with CCMH and the importance of providing treatment if universities want to see them succeed. Dr. Locke summarized his call to universities to expand resources by stating that universities cannot just say "identify and refer... It's refer to what?"

DR. BRIGID CAHILL (UNIVERSITY OF ROCHESTER)

Idealistic, energetic, bubbling with excitement, and eager to make a positive impact: these are the qualities of college students that drew Brigid Cahill in to working on a university campus. Dr. Cahill is the director of the University Counseling Center at the University of Rochester. She enjoys working with undergraduate students who, while exploring and solidifying identities, often come into contact with mental health issues for the first time.

Dr. Cahill received her PhD in clinical-community psychology at the University of South Carolina, and joined the University of Rochester faculty in 2002. There she supervises therapists in training and has had many roles over the years at the counseling center: postdoctoral fellow, outreach coordinator, training director, and now director.

After years of working in the field, it can be easy to become "jaded," she reflected. However, it is moments seeing students' hopelessness transform into hopefulness that makes her job incredibly meaningful. There have been a few different students in particular who come to Dr. Cahill's mind. These are students who have had low moments (e.g., suicide attempts or medical leave). And then—after receiving treatment—come out on the other side with a diploma in hand.

FACING PRESSURES TO KEEP EVERYONE ALIVE

"As much as we would love to, we can't do everything for everybody," Dr. Cahill said. The University of Rochester is unable to sustainably provide long-term treatment. Instead, the counseling center operates on a short-term treatment model. Students with more serious mental health concerns or long-term treatment needs are referred off campus. However, she recognizes that when students are referred off campus, transportation and insurance coverage can become additional barriers. Dr. Cahill is hopeful that a silver lining of the pandemic is the increased use of teletherapy, which may remove transportation as a barrier.

Dr. Cahill reflected on the expectation that counseling centers are expected to be a so-called fix-all: "In general, there is a sense that mental health providers will 'fix' everybody, but we do not have the resources to take care of everyone in the way they need to be."

Across counseling centers in the country, she worries about the pressure that universities place on counseling center staff to keep everyone alive and happy. The reality is that counseling centers just don't have the ability to hold the weight of the world on their shoulders. Dr. Cahill encourages therapists to seek out therapy for their own mental health, to take care of themselves, and to take time to laugh together. While supervision and support are available to counseling center staff, she says those aren't enough.

Dr. Cahill believes that universities have a critical role to play in helping to prevent suicide. They can do this by "making resources available, creating a culture of true self-care... normalizing help seeking, and helping all members of the community have awareness of mental health concerns." She stressed the importance of a university's allocating resources to mental health and suicide prevention. There's always more needed than feasibly can be given—more staff, more therapy, more time, more encouragement to seek care. As for the issue of there never being enough staff in any counseling center, Dr. Cahill admits, "I don't think we can hire our way out of it."

When I asked Dr. Cahill what she thought is the biggest challenge that colleges face in addressing mental health and suicide on their campuses, she said the challenge may even be rewording the question to:

"What are universities and colleges *willing* to do to try to make mental health be a part of the question?"

Her belief, like that of many leaders in this book, is that mental health should be a part of every setting. One of the biggest challenges on campuses for student-led initiatives is the issue of sustainable longevity. With student leaders graduating each year and staff turnover, wellness programs and initiatives can dissolve. As a way to combat this turnover, it is important for younger students and campus partners—not just seniors—to become involved.

Dr. Cahill believes that universities are responsible for providing resources and for setting a positive tone on campus. She thinks they should be working toward creating cultures that support mental health and normalize help-seeking. This responsibility includes setting aside time to listen to college students. In particular, Dr. Cahill supported the formation of a mental health task force. She loves and appreciates the energy of college student mental health advocates, reflecting that it allows her to question things that had previously seemed unquestionable.

RANKINGS AND MENTAL HEALTH SERVICES

High school juniors and seniors are quick to frequent the Princeton Review for rankings on qualities they are looking for in a school. Categories range from academics/administration to politics to social scene.[159] As a high school student, you may have spent hours on your bedroom floor flipping through the *Best 385 Colleges* Princeton Review book, scanning the pages to try to decide which universities to apply to. Did you notice that there is no category for students to rank mental health services?

Thinking about advertising mental health services to potential applicants is a relatively new idea. Dr. Cahill reflects that colleges have been more hesitant to use mental health services as a selling point of advertising for prospective students. This reluctance may come in part from perceived students. She elaborated that it is easier for universities to *"pour money into a research program that will attract the best and brightest students or sports programs that will attract stellar athletes... The selling point of advertising 'We have really excellent mental health resources' doesn't seem to be something that is up there as something that universities and colleges are competing to be the one that has the best services. There's stigma."*

Dr. Cahill says that it would be nice if mental health was reflected as a value in recruiting students to college campuses. Could you imagine if universities began competing with each other for who has the best mental health services? These services would improve substantially because more

159 The Princeton Review, "The Princeton Review's College Ranking Methodology."

funding would be allocated to those entities. And as a result, fewer students would suffer.

DR. WILL MEEK (BROWN UNIVERSITY)

THE POWER OF A SMILE

What if preventing suicide started with smiling to a stranger as you passed them by on the street? According to Dr. Will Meek, one way to immediately begin thinking about shifting the culture on campuses is this minimalist act of kindness. Simply acknowledging someone else's presence as you pass by them with a smile or a nod could make a huge difference in that person's day.

Really take a moment and think about it—is there a random act of kindness that stands out that a stranger did for you? Maybe in the line at the grocery store? Or maybe you were having an off day and someone paused to smile at you? Or even gave you an unexpected compliment?

If everyone begins to acknowledge each other as fellow people in this world, a "different sense of community" can develop— as well as a feeling that you're part of something bigger than yourself. We know that connection, community, and a sense of belonging are protective factors for suicide, while alienation and isolation are huge risk factors.[160] Dr. Meek elaborated on his perspective as a counseling center director:

---

160   American Foundation for Suicide Prevention, "Risk Factors."

"Brown is known as the 'happy' ivy league school, but people don't always feel that way here. It can be really harsh sometimes, too...We're in the counseling center so we see the people who are disconnected and lonely and hurting...

"...Folks in New England seem more in a hurry than people in Oregon. You see more frowns and people avoiding eye contact, and just ignoring the presence of other people around them, sometimes even on campus, like—this is no connection at all. This is not happiness or warmth. This is cold and disconnected, and that has an impact on how we feel in our lives and the spaces we inhabit."

Beginning in 2017, Dr. Meek came into the role as Counseling and Psychological Services director at Brown University; he was and still is determined to bring innovative ideas, listen to student voices, and help make a dent in the demand crisis.

CREATE SPACE FOR INNOVATION

Dr. Will Meek highlighted that the personalities of people working on college campuses will make a difference in the programs that get carried out. While there are some people on the more conservative side in program implementation, there are others who aren't afraid to be innovative in their ideas. As a "punk rock singer" during his youth and a current leader trying to tear down old systems, Dr. Meek relies on innovative, new ideas. On Brown's Counseling and Psychological Services website, there is a list of programming that has been successful and past programming that hasn't worked as well. Examples of successful programming included:

- "Coffee with CAPS" (rotating meet-and-greet with different staff members each week)

- Groups:
    - Support for gender diversity
    - Support for black women
    - DBT skills group

- Student consultation board

- B.E.A.R. Project (aimed at supporting students)

- Accommodation Evaluations

- Trainings
    - Trans Health Training
    - Anti-racism Training

- Anonymous feedback form

- Project LETS (peer training program)[161]

Out of all of the college counseling center websites I have looked at (hovering around 100), this website was in my subjective experience by far one of the easiest to navigate. From my perspective, it was very transparent because there was a list of exactly what is currently working and what wasn't. In addition, there was an entire section dedicated to finding care in the community (i.e., "know what you want, how to pay, where to look, how to set it up, other ideas"). There also

---

161 Brown University, "Labs."

was an entire page dedicated to helping a student in distress (i.e., how to distinguish between stress versus distress versus crisis situations).

Dr. Meek shared that when he presents these innovative ideas at conferences, responses from colleagues are typically varied. About a third of the room says, "Hell yeah, this is cool; I'm doing it!" Another third says, "This seems cool, but how the heck did this guy even get this done?" And the rest of the room says, "Hell no, this is blasphemous and you're ruining psychology."

One of the most critical parts of innovation is listening to student voices for ideas. Dr. Meek shared, "I think students should have a ton of input…As much as I don't like making comparisons to…corporate America…any business needs to listen to what their costumers say…"

There was one particular project he discussed that I want to highlight further because I truly think all colleges could benefit from having a program similar to this one.

THE B.E.A.R. PROJECT
After meeting with over 1,000 students and faculty, Brown's Counseling and Psychological Services created this program, similar to a gatekeeper training, in which students learn how to best support other students who may be at risk. There are in-person trainings as well as information on their website.[162]

---

162 Brown University, "Helping a Student in Distress."

Below is information freely available online as a resource for students:

1.) **B**e Present

"It is easy to go through your day moving from task to task, without paying attention to the people around you. We encourage you to build time into your day to connect with each other (for example, students meeting for a meal, staff getting to know students, faculty leaving time in their schedule after a class in case a student wants to check-in). If you notice that something feels off in one of your interactions, we encourage you to listen to that feeling and use it as a cue to engage."

2.) **E**ngage

"You can't tell how a person is doing or how to help just by looking at them. If you feel worried about a student, we encourage you to attempt to engage with them in order to gain an understanding of what they are going through. Focusing your attention on a student who is upset will likely give you clues of how you can best provide support, and the student is likely to feel more hopeful just because someone is making the space to pay attention to their experience."

Helpful "engage" hints:

- Listen more than talk.

- Use nonverbal cues (for example, nod your head, point your body towards the person) and verbal cues (such as "It sounds like...") to show you are interested in their experience.
- Avoid giving quick solutions.

3.) **A**sk

"If you notice a student who is upset, by interacting with the student, you are well on your way to being seen as support. While engaging with a student, we encourage you to ask open-ended questions about your concern: 'How are you doing?' 'Can you tell me more about that?'

It can be useful to promote the student's sense of agency by asking how you can be helpful: 'Would it be okay if we talk about potential resources that may be helpful for you?'

If you have any sense of worry about the student's safety, we encourage you to ask   directly about your concern: 'Are you thinking about killing yourself?' 'Have you been having thoughts of harming yourself?'

It is a myth that asking a person directly about suicide makes them more likely to consider suicide as an option. Asking a student directly about suicide is useful because it will likely:

- Provide relief for the student who has been thinking about suicide but hasn't been able to talk to anyone about the experience.

- Give you, the helper, information about your next step. When you ask directly about suicide, the student may reassure you that you don't have to worry ('No, I'm stressed, but it's not that bad'), or the student may open up and indicate that suicidal thoughts are part of their experience. Both answers will help you understand together what next steps would be useful.

4.) **R**efer to resources[163]

THE IDIOSYNCRASIES OF A UNIVERSITY

According to Dr. Meek, "shades of grey" exist: people aren't really sure where the line is for preventing suicide on campuses. Some of the barriers that may prevent colleges from preventing suicide include physical resources (i.e., money, time, people). He also touched on the legal climate around suicides on college campuses, and noted that the decisions schools make around suicide often are informed by the law. He elaborated:

"It's not necessarily liability like 'protect the school…' It's more like, 'How can we do what's right and what we're supposed to do?' Like what's the case law that's been going through the courts? What is the school obligated to do? What kind of things should the school do anyway as extra? What should the school not do? If you know there's a student who is really suicidal on campus, you know they should have some kind of assessment

---

163 Ibid.

done. Who does that? How fast? What if they refuse? What happens after that?"

Dr. Meek pointed out that the answers to these questions are "idiosyncratic to each state and each university's history and the way those unique lawyers are reading the current state of affairs." Thus, there is variation depending on the school, the state, and the philosophy of the institution.

WHY COLLEGE STUDENTS?

In terms of responsibility for mental health on a college campus, Dr. Meek's perspective was that "everybody does mental health work." A healthy university climate involves one with compassion, respect, connection, and a sense of community. This goes for students, faculty, and staff. It will look different depending on what your role is on campus. However, each person has a role to play. A sense of community is crucial.

Growing up in an area where many of his childhood friends faced adversity, Dr. Meek saw early the importance of systems. He was motivated to work in an area where he could connect people to the resources that improve their lives. On a broader global scale, many of the people who need mental health treatment are unable to attain it. On college campuses, there is an opportunity to expand resources in an effort to reach the highest number of students possible.

Talking to Dr. Meek gave me hope that college counseling centers can be innovative and creative and listen to student voices. Creating a community and building on the philosophy and programs he has instituted at Brown, colleges have the chance to greatly impact student mental health. We can all start with smiling at the next stranger we see.

DR. GREGORY EELLS (UNIVERSITY OF PENNSYLVANIA)

Dr. Gregory Eells worked as the director of Cornell's counseling center for fifteen years and served on multiple boards advising college mental health organizations. Entering the fall of 2019, he worked at the University of Pennsylvania as the executive director of Counseling and Psychological Services. His perspective is especially invaluable. Below are pieces he shared with me, before his passing, about his perspective on suicide and mental illness on college campuses.

Dr. Eells expressed that, for him, working with college students was a real calling. He specified that one of the most motivating things was that "you can see the difference you make...[college students] are really laying the foundation for the trajectory of where their life is going to go..."

He elaborated that the reason he was in this work was because he saw the impact on students: "...*There's a collection of stories of students who come back and say, 'Wow, that just made a huge difference in my life...and saved me...' Intervening early, and providing mental health care in an accessible way, it does save lives...That's why I'm in college mental health...*"

THE IMPORTANCE OF PROMOTING WELL-BEING

I asked Dr. Eells about his perspective on the biggest challenges that colleges face in addressing mental health and suicide. He defined mental health and suicide as separate but overlapping constructs. The first one he talked about was mental health:

"To define [mental health] from a research perspective, sort of from a clinical perspective...everybody has mental health and struggles with some issues of suffering...All of us can probably benefit from therapy and treatment, or things that you could learn from therapy and psychological constructs to live your life in a more happy way...And then there are people who really need treatment, sometimes medication, a combination of medication management and individual therapy, group therapy..."

From Dr. Eells's perspective, colleges and universities have begun to see the importance of promoting student well-being. He elaborated that students often arrive at college already having had experience with treatment. Dr. Eells stated:

"Today's high school seniors are tomorrow's college freshmen... If you look at clinical data, half of the people who come to counseling centers have already been to therapy before they come to college. So I think there is somehow kind of this myth that high school students are self-actualized by the time they come to college, and then they come to college and the stress of college is what contributes to their suicide risk or eating disorder. And I mean, that isn't my experience as a clinician. People come with incredible treatment histories."

Dr. Eells noted that most colleges have added additional counseling services for their students and that he believes most universities would say that they are responsible for mental health. He explained that colleges and universities are realizing that "you can't have institutions dedicated to the life of learning without attending, to some extent, to mental health."

SUICIDE: CHALLENGES & RESPONSIBILITY

The second part of the question was specifically about whether a college campus is responsible for preventing suicide. We discussed the research on suicide which, as I reiterate throughout this book, is complex. Dr. Eells highlighted that there are often larger sociological factors, such as economic hardship, social disconnection, trauma history, painful life experiences, and social disconnection that "play a huge impact on accounting for variance in suicide rates."

He also shared:

"American culture, every age group, suicide rates are rising—everyone born after the 1960s have showed increases in suicide rates. College students are actually one of the lower groups if you break down age and so forth...I think suicide is far more complex, and it's hard to disentangle from our culture."

Suicide is the second leading cause of death for college-aged students. However, suicide affects people in all age groups. According CDC, in 2017, the national suicide rate was highest among adults between forty-five and fifty-four years of age and the second highest rate occurred for older adults above the age of eighty-five.[164] Dr. Eells commented on differences in response from the public for a college student suicide as opposed to other populations:

---

164 American Foundation for Suicide Prevention, "Suicide Statistics."

"Compared to a county health clinic, someone who has mental illness for twenty years...they don't even get an obituary. [But when a] college student dies by suicide, many times because of the same or similar larger sociological factors, it can become a huge story in the New York Times. *Especially if it is a prestigious school..."*

On the role that universities hold in responsibility for preventing suicide, he said that the question was harder to answer, elaborating, *"Universities still have a role, of course. But do they have the power or control I think they often times get blamed for? No. I mean, that's my experience."*

Dr. Eells emphasized the complexity of the role colleges have for preventing suicide on their campuses. He challenged me to think about whether or not my employer, the psychiatric hospital where I work, would be responsible if I were to die by suicide. Comparing a university setting to a work setting, he said, *"In some ways, it's that relationship... hopefully, they provide you insurance, access to care, those sort of things—which universities, I think, do a better job, than private insurance..."*

ACCESSIBILITY, INSURANCE, AND OTHER BARRIERS TO TREATMENT

Private practice and community mental health are different landscapes in terms of accessibility. In private practice, evidence-based treatment can be extremely effective, but there may be additional barriers to receiving treatment due to financial concerns. In community mental health, serious mental illness may have been in a person's life for years, or even decades, before they arrive at the center to seek treatment. College mental health is unique in that counseling services are included as a part of the tuition. Dr. Eells reflected:

"In spite of what people say, mental health care and health care are complicated because it gets into cost. And universities could provide more care and lower barriers to care—they would have to raise student insurance or student health fees... The cost will always be passed onto students.

"And in all honesty, health fees are actually much more equitable [for college students]. I mean, they are kind of like a single payer system... I think that's often a question for students or a university community: how much do you want to pay? Who pays it? How do you share the cost?"

Cost is a huge factor in health care and is a major barrier to care in mental health services. A single-payer system is a health system in which one entity, such as the government, pays for the cost of health care services. Although cost for students may be less of a barrier because these services may be included in tuition, the services that a counseling center offers are sometimes less specialized.

More complex mental health cases, which require additional treatment not included in the health services fee, are frequently referred off campus. Depending on the school size, they may not have the capacity to treat all of their students. These are the more serious cases that require more time, energy, and resources. Students with more complex and serious issues are being referred off campus and entering the world of private practice, in which cost and lack of insurance coverage frequently becomes a huge barrier.

FRAMEWORKS AND PREVENTION

Shifting gears from treatment to the topic of prevention, I asked if Dr. Eells thought there were barriers that prevented colleges from utilizing the free frameworks for suicide prevention and resources that are available online. As a previous member of JED's advisory board and a partner in working to develop many of the frameworks, he reflected on the utility of these frameworks on college campuses:

"You know, some of it just depends on the staff there—it depends on the director. But I think more and more of that information is getting out and benefiting students. And some of those things could benefit the larger American population. Not to say there aren't barriers, of course, but I think colleges and universities have worked pretty hard to overcome some of those [barriers]."

THE TRICKINESS OF LEAVE OF ABSENCE POLICIES AND STUDENT VOICES

Each year, there are a percentage of students who take a leave—whether for a semester or a year—many due to mental health reasons. The final question I asked was if students had a voice in the mental health related policies (e.g., Leave of Absence) on campus. He emphasized the power of the student perspective, stating, *"Students...should always have a voice."* He explained that student voices are the most powerful in destigmatizing mental illnesses and promoting care. It is, however, more difficult to have a voice in regard to Leave of Absence policies.

Dr. Eells, who had written and presented on this topic, explained the complexity of student voices in these policies. Sometimes students leave of their own accord, but often, when a student is suicidal or academically failing, university staff intervene, and the leave becomes mandatory. Having worked at Cornell and Penn, he commented: *"Cornell's leave policies are complicated. Penn's are [too]...Ivies are all pretty decentralized."*

Having a decentralized system creates challenges in enabling academic departments and counseling centers to work together to determine Leave of Absences. He pointed out that in most colleges and universities, people working in the counseling center are in a bind: a student leave is often an academic decision, not a clinical decision. Dr. Eells reflected;

"Where does the clinical judgement come in?...[The student] with an eating disorder...unless they go to inpatient, their heart can stop—but the person is straight-A student and they're like, 'I don't want to leave...' Leave policies are tricky, they are nuanced...Most colleges and universities are dependent on the academic programs because they are academic decisions. Sometimes even counseling centers with clinical expertise don't have much ability to weigh in because it's an academic decision. But then the academic folks really don't have any clinical judgement at all, nor should they."

And the complexity continues when students want to return to college after their leave. Dr. Eells explained:

"...The health and counseling centers want to be treatment providers...not to be...making forensic decisions predicting whether someone's okay to return or not.

"[Schools] usually need to rely on outside providers. But sometimes outside providers don't have the context. I mean, it's complicated. And the students generally just want to come back. But sometimes coming back is the worst thing. [laughs] I mean, it's hard."

In his experience, Dr. Eells shared that students have varying reactions to Leave of Absence policies. If given a choice between a Leave of Absence or incurring academic consequences, some students initially may feel forced to leave campus. A year later, those same students may say that the time away allowed them to get better. Other students may not want to go home because *"home is the worst place for them... [and] their parents are a major part of the problem."*

LET'S TALK

In an effort to increase support for students who may be hesitant to initially start treatment, Dr. Eells created the Let's Talk program. Originally spearheaded at Cornell, it is now present on roughly one hundred college campuses across the nation.[165] The program is a free and confidential way to talk to a counselor without needing to make an appointment. Students have the ability to stop by the same day that they need to talk to someone. The services are typically free to students as a stepping-stone those who may want support,

---

165 Cornell Health, "Let's Talk Drop-In Consultation"

problem-solving, or more information about counseling services. Let's Talk is just one example of Dr. Eells's positive impact in the field of college mental health, felt by hundreds of schools across the nation.

PART IV:

MY LIVED EXPERIENCES

CHAPTER 11:

COMBINING SPHERES

SONG: "WARRIOR"

ARTIST: DEMI LOVATO

My lived experiences are intentionally a separate part in this book. While I do provide some psychoeducation, this section isn't based primarily on research. Rather, it's a story of my own journey navigating mental health and recovery. I strongly believe that in order to reduce stigma present in the field of clinical psychology and society more broadly, it is critical to use advocacy in a healthy way. Before college, I remained silent, pushing the darkest periods of my past completely out of my mind. Until this section, my research and my lived experiences existed in separate spheres.

When I was in the process of applying for my postbaccalaureate clinical position, I was given the advice that sharing anything related to personal or loved ones' lived experience would be a "kiss of death" for the job interview. I was advised that no one in clinical psychology under any circumstances should ever share their personal "why" for going into the field. Most people have a personal "why," but until a psychologist has built up decades of career experience, only then would it be acceptable to disclose mental health history—and even then, it would still be controversial.

By writing this book as a young person, combining aspects of my lived experience and research, I am trying to break a glass ceiling in the old-school framework of psychology. This framework, which still exists in many places, includes a "not me" mentality when doing research and work in the mental health world.

My passion is fueled, in part, by my experiences and the experiences of those close to me. I know what it's like to have been diagnosed with several psychiatric disorders. I know what it's like to live with scars on my body. I know what it's like to have had people close to me attempt suicide. And I know what it's like to have seriously considered suicide.

For long periods throughout adolescence and young adult life, I was unmistakably not healthy. I lived in a state of "I'm fine," appearing bright to the outside world. I was very resistant to the idea of psychiatric treatment and experienced immense amounts of shame, guilt, and internalized stigma. This next section, a stark contrast to my previously silent self, is an intimate look into my past, with a focus on recovery, healing, and breaking stereotypes.

Writing this chapter scares me because I don't know how you, the reader, will react. Sharing my story goes against everything that my OCD tries to control. Thoughts scream in my mind: *"What if I won't get accepted into graduate school? What if everyone hates me for sharing? Judges who I am? Becomes mad at me? What if my psychology and public health career comes to a halt?"*

All of these fears are a large part of the reason I am writing. There are people working in clinical psychology, public health, research, neuroscience, epidemiology, and related fields who have lived experience with mental health issues. There are even people working in this field who die by suicide.

It is my hope that in being open, you may connect to my human experience—whether it be through yourself, a loved one, or someone you know. It is my hope that my story will add credibility to the research, advocacy, and policy work that I do surrounding mental health and suicide prevention. No one has the same story. Each one of us has a different life experience and relationship to mental health. What brings us together is that at the end of the day, we are all human, and even if you cannot relate directly to my personal story, you may relate to aspects of my human experience.

When I first started speaking up about mental health, those around me were surprised that the bubbly, outgoing, smiley person that the outside world so often sees is not the only part of me. Throughout my life, even in darker times, people have told me that I am the happiest person they have ever met. The reality is that the intensity of my joy is very real, as is the intensity of my more unwanted emotions. The difference is that, for a long time before therapy, I felt I had to experience my sadness, fear, and anger alone. Intense work on myself allowed me to reach a place where I feel comfortable accepting my experiences, while also recognizing that my experiences do not define who I am at my core.

Identities are often multifaceted. Pieces of my identity include being a runner, an older sister, a nature lover, a little bit of a free spirit, and a mental health advocate. This next section focuses on the latter. Sometimes, when we think of the term "mental illness," we think of someone who is unable to fit in with the rest of society. However, in my own experience, mental illness or mental health obstacles can scream silently. On paper, I fit the mold of a hardworking student. Varsity athlete and honors student, graduating in the top of my high school class, I journeyed through an academically rigorous college. There I engaged in activities that added an immense amount of meaning to my life: I was president and later advised a community service club, played on our women's club soccer team, mentored incoming international students, guided mediation classes, taught leadership workshops, was a research assistant in clinical psychology, worked for our Health Promotion Office, completed a community engagement capstone, led a group of students to Honduras for an alternative spring break trip, and worked for our city's Department of Recreation and Youth services. From afar, I look like every other busy student on an academically rigorous college campus—balancing multiple jobs, extracurriculars, social life, and school. But I live with mental health issues. And I talk about it.

With that, welcome to my "kiss of death."

CHAPTER 12:

BREAKING
STEREOTYPES

———

In this chapter, I elaborate on my personal experiences to break stereotypes about obsessive-compulsive Disorder (OCD), eating disorders (ED), and non-suicidal self-injury (NSSI).

On campus, I hear other students use OCD as an adjective:

"I'm *soooooo* OCD."

"I need to be more OCD about my notes for this class."

"We should all have a little more OCD."

Because of this, I intentionally spend a good chunk of this chapter talking about my experiences with obsessive compulsive disorder. The hope is that my story gives you a glimpse into true realities of what it can be like to live with OCD.

OBSESSIVE-COMPULSIVE DISORDER (OCD)

SONG: "SIMPLE SONG"

ARTIST: MILEY CYRUS

OCD feels like having a war in your brain that the outside world cannot always see. Every thought is intense and circles rapidly. To make the obsession stop immediately and instantaneously, there's an easy fix: a compulsion.

My parents first started to notice my obsessions and compulsions in the third grade, when I was nine years old. For a child, it is very common to see the world as black and white. For a child with OCD, these stark boundaries and rules are even more rigid. When I was eight years old, I had some anxiety (e.g., going any amount over the speed limit, thinking people didn't like me, worrying teachers were angry with me), but my fears really escalated to a new level when I first started the DARE program at school.

My younger brother always jokes that the DARE program "screwed me over." The DARE (Drug Abuse Resistance Education) curriculum came into our elementary school with the vision for "a world in which students everywhere are empowered to respect others and choose lives free from violence, substance use, and other dangerous behaviors."[166] The police officers and other authority figures taught us that alcohol was "bad." My OCD became hooked, stuck on this notion that all alcohol—under any circumstances—was dangerous.

---

166 Drug and Alcohol Resistance Education, "About D.A.R.E."

My compulsions around alcohol varied. If food was on the same counter with alcohol, I couldn't eat the food, for fear that the beer had contaminated it. At restaurants, I wouldn't drink my beverage unless one of my parents tested it first to ensure that the waiter hadn't accidentally spiked it with liquor. There was one point when I would not eat a cookie because of the alcohol found in vanilla extract. At family gatherings, I'd avoid the room where alcohol was served, and avoid even looking at alcohol. The exception to this was a compulsion to count how many drinks my parents had consumed.

My parents weren't big drinkers. However, like many parents, they would occasionally have a glass of wine or a beer at night. When we went out to family parties or barbecues, they sometimes would have more than one glass. When counting my parents' drinks, if it was one drink, I normally would be okay. If it was two or more drinks throughout the course of the night, I'd become hysterical. I was petrified. Alcohol was "bad," which meant my parents were "bad," and I didn't know what to do.

When the obsessions first started, my parents knew I was scared of alcohol, so they started hiding any bottles from my sight. One night, I found a beer bottle my dad had hidden behind the couch in our family room. I was so upset, I grabbed the green Yuengling beer bottle and threw it as hard as I could against the stone fireplace. It shattered into pieces with shards of glass scattering, causing me to scream, panic, and sob—leading my parents to realize my extreme level of distress and recognize that we needed professional help.

In the OCD world, the act of my dad changing his behavior (i.e., hiding his beer bottle) to avoid triggering my OCD is known as accommodation. Therapists work with parents of kids with OCD to make them aware of accommodation—which though it's intuitive to want to prevent your child's distress, is actually not as helpful in the long run.

Shortly after the beer bottle incident, I started going to a psychologist who specialized in OCD, also known to me as the "worry doctor." The "worry doctor" was a forty-five-minute drive away. My mom explained that just like kids needed to see a regular doctor, I had to see a doctor to help with my "worry brain." Dr. Tamar Chansky helped me learn to recognize the difference between my worry brain (OCD) and my brain (Emily).[167]

In therapy, I vividly remember doing what I now know is referred to as "exposure" in exposure and response prevention therapy. OCD exposures, out of context, are often very strange. The first exposure I did was viewing pictures of beer bottles on a poster for a set amount of time without looking away. Another exposure involved me touching a pretzel to the side of a beer bottle and then eating the pretzel. And in one exposure, I watched my mom while she drank a sip of beer. Taking a step back for a second, just to note how bizarre this may seem: as a fifth grader, a part of my treatment was literally to sit in an office and watch my mom take a sip of alcohol.

---

167 Chansky, Tamar, *Freeing Your Child From Obsessive-Compulsive Disorder.*

It may seem silly that sitting in a room with a beer bottle elicited such panic and discomfort for a ten-year-old. However, for someone with obsessive-compulsive disorder, thoughts and obsessions can elicit a "fight, flight, or freeze" fear response in the brain. Every person on this earth has a fear response (*see a bear: RUN!*). The warning system in our brains can be very helpful for managing crisis situations. However, for someone with OCD, the brain flags specific thoughts as dangerous when there may or may not actually be danger present. A siren goes off that it's important to pay more attention to those thoughts, and the warning system is suddenly faulty.

It's wild to realize that each person has up to sixty thousand thoughts per day.[168] As humans, we have intrusive or unwanted thoughts and images that suddenly pop into our minds. The difference is that for a brain with OCD, intrusive thoughts are stickier than they would be in a brain without OCD. One analogy is to think of a pasta strainer. The vast majority of brains allow intrusive thoughts to flow like water through the holes of the strainer. However, a brain with untreated OCD will not allow the thoughts to go through the strainer. The thoughts get "stuck" until completing the compulsion, which then allows them to flow through.

Picture this:

You are driving on the highway and the thought, "I could drive my car off the side of the road," pops into your head.

---

168 TLEX Institute, "How to Effortlessly."

You might have a subsequent thought, "Huh, that was strange," and continue driving.

For a brain with harm OCD, this thought may be more distressing, evokes a stronger emotional reaction, and becomes stuck. The thought may pop into your head, "I could drive my car off the side of the road," followed by racing thoughts: "What is wrong with me? Does having that thought mean I do want to kill myself and the others in my car? What if I actually *did* drive my car off the side of the road? I need to get rid of this thought and do XYZ [compulsion] to make sure that I don't want to harm others."

The really cool thing about OCD treatment is that it is effective. About 70 percent of people who receive treatment, medication, or therapy will show an improvement in symptoms.[169] Try telling fifth grade Emily that present-day me enjoys the taste of Sangria, and I would have laughed in disbelief. You can never truly "cure" OCD because you can't altogether get rid of obsessive thoughts. However, you can work to change your relationship to the thoughts, to accept the thoughts as separate from yourself, and hold power in not giving in to the compulsions.

Many people, when they think of obsessive-compulsive disorder, picture a spotless room or someone who washes their hands a lot. This makes sense, because for many people with OCD, cleanliness and hygiene can be severe obsessions and compulsions. However, there are actually many subtypes of OCD and even within the categories, there is variety.

---

169 International OCD Foundation, "How is OCD Treated?"

The Peace of Mind Foundation outlines the following subtypes:

- Counting and checking
- Germs and contamination
- Harm intrusive thoughts
- Immoral or scrupulosity
- Magical thinking
- Perfectionism or "just right"
- Postpartum OCD
- Relationship OCD
- Somatic OCD[170]

Most people engage in some form of repeated behaviors (your sports team says the cheer before the start of each game, you wear your favorite pair of socks for "good luck," you double check to make sure the door is locked before leaving the house, etc.). This doesn't mean that most people have "a little bit of OCD."[171] To meet criteria for an OCD diagnosis, obsessions and compulsions must be time-consuming (typically more than one hour per day up to the entire day), cause significant distress, and interfere with daily functioning or activities that the person values.[172]

ELEMENTARY SCHOOL: "WORRY" AND JOY

I can promise you that OCD isn't only about washing your hands or keeping an organized, color-coded notebook. To

---

170 Peace of Mind, "What is OCD."

171 "What is OCD?" International OCD Foundation, "What is OCD?"

172 Psychiatry, "What is Obsessive Compulsive Disorder?"

give concrete examples that break the stereotypical image of OCD, below I listed a sampling of some of the obsessions and compulsions that entered into my own life during elementary school in addition to the one about alcohol:

OCD told me I might accidentally hurt or kill someone. To avoid harming others, I sat with my feet pointed inward away from people, looked at each person in a room for the same number of seconds, pointed my pencil away from people, avoided touching my thumb to my index finger so my hand would not resemble anything close to a gun, and smiled a specific way.

OCD told me I had to be "healthy." For example, I avoided stepping on cigarettes while playing soccer because OCD told me doing so was the same as smoking and "unhealthy." Once, when I realized that I wasn't as diligent in my scanning of the field for cigarettes, I knew there was a chance that I could have stepped on a cigarette. Even though we were running late, the next practice, panic-stricken, I adamantly refused to wear my cleats again until my mom sanitized them.

OCD told me I had to sit in the *right* chair in class, choose the *right* Build-A-Bear from the bin, lift my feet in the shower the *right* number of times, say goodnight to my parents and my stuffed animals the *right* way, scratch the itches of our golden retriever Cassidy the *right* way.

Deep down I felt like no one understood me. I *knew* that I was right no matter how much my family tried to use logic to say I was being irrational. *"Emily. Nothing is happening.*

You're fine. Stop worrying," my dad told me in a genuine effort to try to bring my anxiety down. It didn't work. Trying to logic your way out of OCD only exacerbates it.

It was extremely difficult for me to verbalize any of my obsessions or compulsions. My mom encouraged me to write them down to her, often back and forth, in a journal. Below are journal entries from my fifth grade year (2006) after beginning therapy:

"I feel like a bad person. I cannot smile. I cannot make my thumb touch my index finger. I cannot live with Worry anymore...See when I do that thingy with my hand Worry somehow told me that it meant kill or hurt. Because you know the thingy with your hand does mean that. I think that I should be able to handle this, but I just wanted to see if you [mom] could help me...Also the pencil thingy too, I'm trying to handle that too.

"I feel sick of Worry. I will try to answer some of your [mom] questions, but not all. The barrette, pencils don't bother me as much as the sporks and scissors (mostly sporks). The spork looks sort of like a pitch fork so I always have to point it at me or it means that I'm a horrible person. It's sometimes difficult to always point it at myself. Worry says that if I do not wash my hands then I am a germ spreader (that I want to spread germs) (It doesn't hurt to wash your hands you know).

"Why I hate Worry: 1) Worry distracts me from what I am doing. Ex: When [teacher] was calling my table to come up I just sat there. I heard what she was saying, but I was so focused on Worry that I just sat there. 2) I'm not happy. Ex: [teacher]

asked me twice if I was ok. The second time she wanted to know if I wanted to eat lunch with her.

"I am not a bad person. I am not a bad person."

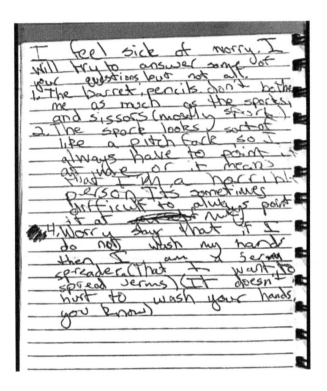

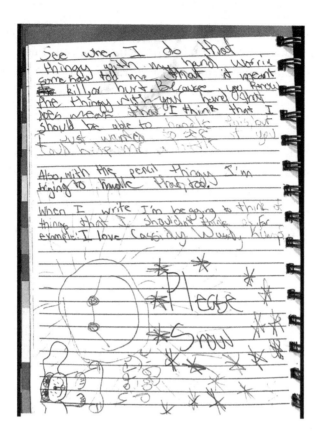

Worry and Emily both living within the same page. My journal entry is a representation of both my minds at the time. As you are learning through my story, there was evidently a lot of anxiety and worry present in my life. However, there was also a kid—a kid who lit up at the thought of snow days, smiled at being with our dog Cassidy, somersaulted on the gymnastics floor, felt empowered on the soccer field, and was happy to doodle pictures of the sun.

OCD treatment for kids focuses on teaching kids that they can experience the fears that their warning system tells them to avoid. They can feel the anxiety and the discomfort, and learn that it won't actually kill them. They can simultaneously experience joy and discomfort, while moving forward in resisting compulsions or rituals in order to be able to engage in childhood enjoyable activities.

As a kid, many of my activities were spent with my younger brother, Ryan, and my childhood best friend, Natalie. We went sledding in winter, played Mario Kart on a Game-Cube, climbed trees together, made up games to play outside, laughed in Nat's swimming pool, bounced on the trampoline, and went on early morning trips to Cracker Barrel.

Ryan saw a side of me that I don't think anyone else saw—as a sibling, he saw not just my happy moments. He lived with me through moments of intense anger, pain, and suffering. Siblings' experiences are often overlooked when discussing and researching mental health, so I FaceTimed Ry to ask if he had any reflections about my OCD that he wanted me to include in the book. Laughing in little brother fashion, he said, "Well, you were an 'expletive' to be around." We then talked for forty minutes about the difficulties of growing up with a sibling who had severe OCD, and discussed the rituals that my OCD would drag him into (e.g., if he didn't position his feet the *right* way on car rides, I would become upset; if he was breathing too loud, I would begin to yell). At the end of the conversation, he reflected, "Even though we were at odds at times, there was nobody I would have rather spent my childhood with." (*I promise I didn't ask him to say this.*)

Natalie and I spent almost every day together in the summers growing up, so she also saw aspects of me that other friends didn't always see. For example, Nat knew that I thought coffee was "bad," which equated to my avoidance of all coffee shops. One day, she encouraged me to challenge that fear.

Nat, Ryan, my mom, and I were walking outside on our way to our local ice cream place when we passed by a Starbucks. Nat pointed to the building and told me to touch it, without me knowing it was a coffee shop. Nat exclaimed, "HA! You just touched Starbucks! You touched coffee!" I recently texted Nat to see if she has as vivid of a memory of that day as I do. She reflected about our childhood together:

"I remember being scared that you'd be mad at me, but I also remember seeing your face when you realized nothing happened after touching the wall. It's interesting looking back because in hindsight as a child, I didn't realize how serious it was or how much distress you were in. I vividly remember sitting in your room and you telling me that you had a journal that you would write your problems in and you told me that there was something wrong with you. In my mind, you just really didn't like certain things and that was you."

SONG: "I CAN'T BREATHE"

ARTIST: BEA MILLER

OCD has changed throughout my life, with new symptoms emerging again at the end of high school. Nat reflected on our high school years:

"I really just thought you were strict about rules for yourself and made sure that you ate well for sports etc....to be honest I remember thinking that you had everything so together and that I should be more like you..."

The following is a glimpse into my inner reality of a few of OCD's rules and what it would mean to "be more like me":

OCD caused me to pick my skin to the point that I ended up in the emergency room. At the time, I thought it was a physical illness. One ER trip and three dermatologists later, I was told I had excoriation disorder (a.k.a. chronic skin-picking, a mental health disorder related to OCD). It was not uncommon for strangers to ask me if I had a disease. My freshman orientation week of college: "Hi! What's your major? What dorm do you live in? Are your legs okay?"

OCD warned that I might not be able to control harming myself. OCD warned me to avoid where the knives were in the kitchen. OCD warned me to run faster across bridges on trail runs in the park. OCD got stuck on intrusive images. (Note: this is different than active suicidal ideation; this is harm OCD, fear of harming myself or others).

OCD told me my runs had to end in 0.02 or they didn't count.

OCD told me I couldn't make *any* mistakes. OCD told me that everyone hated me. OCD told me to punish myself if I made a mistake, said the "wrong" thing, or upset someone.

OCD's warning siren blared like a piercing emergency signal when I thought someone "could be mad" at me. The compulsions around this varied.

OCD even tried to hijack my treatment: *"What if it's all in your head and you don't actually have OCD? What if there is really just something inherently wrong with who you are? Are you sure you're doing treatment right?"*

As a child, I learned through counseling that I lived with "Worry" in my brain, but the first time I truly grasped how fast the thoughts in my head move compared to the general population was actually during freshman year of college. I watched a video with a friend in my freshman dorm room of what a mind with OCD feels like. I turned to her and asked, "Wait, your thoughts don't move that fast?" She responded by expressing gratitude for not living inside my brain.

OCD "rules" morph and change over time. I have accepted that OCD is a part of my story and will never completely be "cured." However, because of therapy, I have the tools in my toolbox to recognize when new ones pop up, and I am now confident in my ability to handle them. I'll give an example from a few hours ago. I am staying at a hostel in California as I write today. This afternoon, before heading out for a hike, I had to decide what items from my backpack to place in the locker and which items could remain in the bag. When holding a bottle of Tylenol from my bag, OCD told me, *"Emily, you need to lock the Tylenol. If not, it means someone could find it in your bookbag and overdose, and you would be responsible for killing them. Do you want to kill them?"* OCD told me I needed to lock up the Tylenol. However, I was able to recognize that this was an obsession, and resisted giving in to the compulsion. OCD used to control my life, consuming hours of my day. Now, I am steering my decisions—not my OCD.

EATING DISORDER (ED)

SONG: "MY WORST ENEMY"

ARTIST: HAILEY KNOX

Eating disorders (ED) are sneaky. It took me a long time to even recognize ED as real, as my inner critic voice was loud and ready to take over: *"You don't even look like someone with an eating disorder. Are you sure you do the behaviors enough times to meet criteria for a diagnosis? What if it's all in your head and you're making it up?"* OCD, internalized stigma, and images the media often portrays of what a person with an eating disorder "looks like" only exacerbate ED's power.

Without going too much into detail about eating disorder behaviors and thoughts, it's important to mention that for a long time, ED has tried very hard to hijack moments of my life. In high school, ED developed rigid rules around what, how, and when I could eat. Many of these rules carried into college. College students—typically—love food. However, at social gatherings and restaurant celebrations throughout college, I could be physically present, but mentally in a different world. If I was deep in thought about food and you talked to me, there was a good chance that I wouldn't hear you right away. Because of the anxiety I experienced eating out around others, I often avoided it all together. I quickly slipped into unhealthy cycles of what took me a while to identify and fully accept as an eating disorder. And treatment for ED was difficult in that OCD developed rituals around any sort of meal planning worksheet that doctors would hand me.

I tried to explain the difficulty of meal planning worksheets to the doctor in my college health center. She encouraged me to continue to try to use the meal plan, even though my OCD latched onto the rigidity and in turn increased my ED symptoms. In an effort to feel more heard, I later decided to make an appointment with our college counseling center. The way our counseling center is set up is that a student makes an initial intake appointment, then a counselor recommends the best course of action. After telling them my symptoms and history, I was told that the best option was to find a counselor off campus who could provide treatment. Because I didn't have a car and with limited public transportation options (Uber didn't yet exist), I had no way to access the treatment they recommended.

I felt defeated. It had taken a lot of courage for me to take the elevator up to the third floor of the counseling center. And at the time, I didn't understand why they weren't willing to treat me. At orientation, they had said to go to the counseling center if you needed help. I went, and they told me to find care elsewhere. They did, however, offer an alternative to individual treatment: "Mood and Food" group therapy. Somewhat fearful, but with no other options, I decided to try it out. In this group, I met other students who were also struggling, and I saw that I wasn't alone in rules around food controlling my life.

BREAKING FREE FROM ED

SONG: "BEAUTIFUL GIRL"

ARTIST: WILLIAM FITZSIMMONS

Recovery for disordered eating ebbs and flows, with the first step being acceptance—acceptance that ED was real and acceptance that my behaviors, feelings, and rules around food weren't helpful or aligned with creating long-term goals for my life. Disordered eating is also tricky in that sometimes people in the environment and society at large reinforce unhealthy behavior patterns through comments about appearance or losing weight.

We need food to survive. Unlike some other addictive behaviors, a big focus on recovery for disordered eating is on changing the relationship to food, rather than eliminating food entirely. There are behaviors surrounding ED that can be cut out entirely, but food itself cannot be.

In the book *Life Without Ed: How One Woman Declared Independence from Her Eating Disorder and How You Can Too,* author Jenni Schaefer speaks about a therapeutic technique that "involves thinking of the eating disorder as a distinct being with unique thoughts and a personality separate" from yourself.[173] She describes her eating disorder as a personified Ed, stating, "Ed was abusive, controlling, and never once hesitated to tell me what he thought, how I was doing it wrong, and what I should be doing instead. I hated him, but I could not leave him."[174] She touches on the pervasiveness of Ed in our culture:

"Ed is the one who stares back at you in the mirror and says you should be dissatisfied with your appearance. Ed talks to all of us. While some of us are deeply embroiled in a relationship with him, others are just casually dating him. Maybe you are just meeting Ed for the first time. Whether you are married to Ed or just flirting with him, this book is for you."[175]

I personally found this book incredibly helpful in my recovery. Below is a Facebook post I wrote during college, at a time when I was at an earlier stage of recovery with ED:

"NEDA [National Eating Disorder Awareness] week starts tomorrow. I'm going to share a small piece of my story with disordered eating. The reason why I'm sharing is because for a very, very long time I felt alone and was not willing to admit there was a problem. And because the stigma surrounding these disorders is very much real. I feel like I sound like a broken record, but I really, really wish someone would have told me this earlier: you are not alone.

---

173 Jenni Schaefer, *Life Without Ed: How One Woman Declared Her Independence from Her Eating Disorder and How You Can Too,* 1.

174 Ibid.

175 Ibid.

"I've had an unhealthy relationship with food for as long as I can remember. In third grade, I had to pick all the salt off of pretzels because salt was "bad" (OCD likes to map onto good/ bad). It started with salt on pretzels and eventually creeped into every food in my life—if it was a "good food," I could eat it. But if I ever ate a "bad food," I would feel absolutely ashamed and extremely self-critical.

"I'm slowly working on forming a healthy relationship with food. Over the past few years, going to restaurants has become easier. But I would be lying if I said that food doesn't have a large control over my life. Mindfulness and yoga have helped a lot. But it's hard...hard to remove the years of rules and societal expectations. It's also really hard to post this. But the more we talk about these things, the more the stigma goes away. The cool thing is, I really do think the media is changing in a good way when it comes to body image and food. Food is fuel. You should eat what makes you feel good. Listening to your body and hunger cues is something that many people, unhealthy relationship with food or not, have gotten away from. And on that note, I'm going to listen to my body and enjoy some ice cream because it is what will make me feel good in this moment. ☺ #NEDA #NEDAweek"

Food doesn't control every aspect of my day anymore. Hard work has helped me reach a place where I no longer hate my body, and no longer feel as trapped by my eating disorder. It's not perfect—it's recovery. There are ups and there are downs, but my power lies in not linking my self-worth to the food I eat.

Both in society more broadly (such as on a college campus), people often talk about "good" foods, "bad" foods, diets, losing weight, gaining weight, eating to relieve stress, skipping meals to study for exams, and other eating behaviors quite frequently. The National Eating Disorder Association (NEDA) estimates that 10 to 20 percent of females and 4 to 10 percent of males will experience an eating disorder during college.[176] Eating disorders can include a combination of restricting, binging, or purging in response to eating. For college students, one of the most common ways to socialize is over food. Yet for those with disordered eating, meals around others can become quite difficult. There are so many young adults, of *all* genders, who experience disordered eating. Contrary to popular belief, disordered eating is rarely only about the food itself, and doesn't exclusively affect women.

NONSUICIDAL SELF-INJURY (NSSI)

SONG: "BETTER DAYS"

ARTIST: THE GOO GOO DOLLS

I went back and forth on including my personal experiences with nonsuicidal self-injury (NSSI). Then, I read a research article that helped me realize it needed to be written about. The article is titled, "Putting the 'Self' in Self-injury Research: Inclusion of People With Lived Experience in the Research Process," and was released by leading NSSI researchers.[177] They argued that the stigma surrounding NSSI among health professionals may be hindering advances in research. This

---

176 Best Colleges, "Understanding Eating Disorders"

177 Lewis et al., "Putting the 'self.'"

stigma exists even among therapists, in that some clinicians will not treat patients with a known history of NSSI. NSSI is estimated to have prevalence for 7.5 to 46.5 percent of adolescents.[178] That's a large percentage of young people who are sometimes blocked from receiving help due to therapists' fears.

NSSI is defined as "the deliberate, self-inflicted destruction of body tissue resulting in immediate damage, **without** suicidal intent."[179] Common examples of NSSI include cutting, scratching, burning, and head-banging. At first glance, NSSI is very counterintuitive—why would anyone want to intentionally hurt themselves when humans are biologically wired to protect themselves from danger and harm?

The science behind NSSI dives into what happens in your brain when you self-injure. According to Cornell's research center for self-injury and prevention, when a person cuts or self-injures, the brain releases feel-good chemicals.[180] These chemicals released by the action of NSSI can often decrease the intensity of emotional pain. For many people, self-harm urges are very strong because of the body's physiological reaction toward immediate relief.

One common misconception is that teenagers only self-harm in order to bring attention to themselves or to manipulate others. However, research suggests that there are more than a

---

178 Cipriano et al., "Nonsuicidal Self-injury: A Systematic Review."

179 "About Self Injury," Self-Injury and Recovery Resources, College of Human Ecology, Cornell University.

180 Ibid.

dozen different functions to NSSI, and the majority of adolescents and young adults engage in NSSI for myriad reasons.[181] Some of these functions include decreasing negative emotional intensity, increasing feelings of autonomy, punishing oneself, stopping dissociation, stopping suicide, and interpersonal communication.[182] Adolescents most commonly engage in NSSI to regulate emotions—in other words, to feel better.

Before I applied skills and techniques to manage my intense thoughts and emotions, cutting provided an immediate relief to emotional pain. It helped give me control when events in my life felt out of my control. It temporarily quieted my suicidal thoughts. And it sometimes served the function of punishing myself after I had made a perceived mistake or if I was angry at myself for possibly upsetting someone. It ultimately helped me feel better—a lot better, immediately—which is why NSSI for many people, myself included, was very hard to stop.

NSSI is clearly not healthy and can be very dangerous. According to the Crisis Text Line, common consequences of NSSI can include potentially needing medical attention, infection, permanent scars, guilt or shame, a diminished sense of self, an addiction to the behavior, avoidance of friends or family, ostracization, and interpersonal difficulty from lying to others about injuries.[183]

---

181 Klonsky et al., "The Functions of Nonsuicidal Self-Injury."

182 Ibid.

183 Crisis Text Line, "How to Deal with Self Harm?"

In the fall of 2019, I stood in front of the incoming Class of 2022 at my university and gave a speech to 1,500 students in which I labeled pieces of my mental health history: "I will be sharing broad experiences of mental health…including self-injury." Before that day, there were only a few people who knew I struggled with self-harm. Up to then, I had hidden it.

I am talking about it because some studies estimate prevalence rates of NSSI in college students to be about 20 percent.[184] In a classic freshman lecture hall of two hundred students, that would mean forty people in the class have intentionally harmed themselves at some point in their life. I'll say that again—one-fifth of college students have engaged in nonsuicidal self-injury. From my eyes, given that a fifth of college students have lived experience with NSSI, it needs to be seen as a public health issue.

---

184 Whitlock et al., "Non-Suicidal Self-Injury on College Campuses."

CHAPTER 13:

UNCOVERING THE MASK

SONG: "TOURNIQUET"

ARTIST: EVANESCENCE

Tragically, there are hundreds and hundreds of stories, and whether directly or indirectly, around humans touched by suicide. It's a part of humanity that has existed for thousands of years. Hearing or maybe even reading the word "suicide" on this page can elicit an emotional response.

It is important, however, that stories with lived experience of suicide are portrayed. I feel very strongly about the way suicide is portrayed in the media, written about in blogs, or otherwise posted about on the Internet. I've read articles in which people share details about their own stories in an effort to decrease stigma, but the reality is that study after study has shown that sharing graphic details about suicidal ideation, attempts, or methods has been linked to increased suicide risk. Thus, although the images in my head were graphic, I intentionally am not including very specific details of my suicidal ideation.

"It was the best of times, it was the worst of times…," says Charles Dickens in *A Tale of Two Cities.*[185]

The reality is that the intensity of my joy is very real, as is the intensity of my more unwanted emotions.

High school consisted of some of my happiest, high-on-life moments at the same exact time that it included excruciating, painful moments of deep suffering. When I started advocating openly about mental health in college, a few of my friends from high school had a "Wait…what?!" response. None of my friends knew me the way my younger brother described as "an [expletive] to be around." On a typical day, you'd never know that during my senior year of high school there were moments when I did not want to be alive. You would never know that there were moments of suffering when suicide seemed like the only path out. How could you?

On paper, I was a highly functioning seventeen-year-old. During my darkest moments, it was common for me to do the following: spend the week going to practice (track or field hockey or soccer), engage in hours of AP homework, work (babysitting or at our local grocery store), and laugh while out with friends. I went to a large public high school and rarely missed a day of school. If "wearing a mask on the

---

185   Charles Dickens, *A Tale of Two Cities* (New York: Chelsea House Publishers, 1987), 1.

harder days" were a class, like all my classes, my goal was to do it perfectly.

Contrary to what you might think when you picture an adolescent who experiences suicidal ideation, most days I wasn't overtly depressed. When I was adventuring with friends exploring nature or hanging out at starry night bonfires, I would feel a lightness in my heart, and have a genuine smile across my face. I was still very passionate about my extracurricular activities, and I never had a premeditated plan to kill myself.

However, I did experience moments of high emotional intensity at home. That's when the suicidal ideation crept in. Looking back, it was scary because my reactions to manage these intense thoughts and emotions were both impulsive and dangerous. I engaged in unhealthy coping behaviors in an effort to avoid and alleviate my pain. Unhealthy coping can be effective for immediate relief in the short term, but extremely detrimental in the long term.

Acceptance and commitment therapy (ACT) uses a beach ball analogy to describe the detrimental effects of trying to suppress or avoid our emotional experiences. Have you ever tried to push a beach ball underneath the water in the swimming pool? You can press it down, but then it pops back up above the surface. So you try again, pushing down on the beach ball harder. And when you inevitably let go of your grip from the beach ball, it skyrockets into the air even higher than before.[186]

The more I tried to push away my emotions, the more they came back—and each wave hit me with stronger force. Stress, combined with increasing OCD, ED, anxiety symptoms, and a lack of sleep from a heavy course load led to "skyrocketing" at home. In excruciating mental pain from my increasing mental health issues, there were times when I couldn't see a way out. In these moments of high distress, the thought of suicide was a comfort. I wanted so badly to escape the intense pain of my symptoms. I felt very much like a burden to my family and friends. In these moments, I truly, genuinely believed the world would be much better off without me in it.

You may have noticed that I have repeatedly said "moments." This is intentional to show that I was not in a state of depression or continuously suicidal for months on end. But when I did experience suicidal ideation, in these moments, the desire to take my life was at the forefront of my mind. I would break down at home (e.g., panic attack, crying, sobbing, screaming, unhealthy coping behaviors). Breaking down only amplified my feelings of guilt and shame, which led to engaging in unhealthy coping to alleviate those feelings. Then came guilt and shame again. I was stuck in a cycle and in complete denial of the seriousness of my experiences.

I was in denial in part because at school and around others, I truly did feel like "myself" (a.k.a. the bubbly Emily that other

---

186 "Acceptance and Commitment Therapy," SOHO, CBT and Mindfulness Center

people saw). On the days that I didn't feel like "myself," I'd hold it together enough that no one else would notice, and then would break down at home. It was in these moments—alone by myself and not knowing how to cope—that waves began to pummel me against a wall. It became harder and harder to access "myself" as the moments became more frequent. I tried so hard to convince not only the other people around me, but also myself that I was okay: "*Emily, you're fine. This isn't a problem.*" But clearly there was a *huge* problem. I wanted to badly hurt myself. I didn't want to exist on Earth anymore. The thought of suicide gave me relief. I felt alone in my experience because I hadn't ever heard anyone at high school ever talk about mental health. I felt hopeless, trapped by my thoughts and feelings. I honestly don't have the words to describe the pain other than saying it felt like living hell.

Living in this excruciating pain, I still wanted absolutely nothing to do with mental health treatment, and wanted to tell no one besides my immediate family. I was resistant because I had already seen "the worry doctor" in elementary school and thought I was "done with that." In full transparency, there was also a stubborn part of me that just didn't want to go. Even at my lowest points, I still felt like I *should* be able to handle everything on my own.

My parents pushed hard for me to go to therapy. They could see that I was clearly in pain and were absolutely determined to get me into treatment, despite my resistance. I eventually did begin to see a young, warm social worker with experience in mindfulness who helped me regain my footing. In therapy, I started to learn healthier coping strategies and created a list of things I had to do when the urges to engage in unhealthy behaviors came up (1. Go for a run 2. Listen to music 3. Call someone 4. Hold an ice cube 5. Use mindfulness skills). She also encouraged me to start medication. With medication and therapy, the "moments" became less and less frequent. I began to access my true self and to see the beauties in my life again. Kelly was the exact person I didn't know I needed.

YOU ARE NOT A BURDEN.

SONG: "HEAD ABOVE WATER"

ARTIST: AVRIL LAVIGNE

If you open up my high school yearbook, the very first entry at the top of the page is from a friend who had only seen me from one angle and said, "*By far the nicest and most collected person I've ever met in my life. I know you're gonna go far in life so just keep doing what you're doing.*"

His words were very kind. Reading my yearbook in retrospect, I realize now that had I "kept doing" what I was doing (i.e., resisting psychiatric treatment, breaking down at home, wearing a "mask" on the harder days at school), I honestly believe that I would have continued down a path that would have ultimately ended in suicide.

There were only a few people who knew that I was seeing a counselor. As the "most collected person," no one could learn the truth know about my inner demons. I felt embarrassed and ashamed for needing to start psychiatric treatment. Another part of me falsely believed that starting treatment meant there was something inherently "wrong" with who I was as a person.

And then, one day, I totally lost my grip of the beach ball at school. It was a day when I had made a "mistake," OCD was screaming, and suicidal ideation came crashing through. Because my emotions were so high, trying to remember details of this day are difficult. However, I talked to my friend Bunny, who related to me what happened. In the middle of class, I walked out of the building before the day had ended. I texted her that I had made a mistake, that I thought I was going to be rescinded from college [catastrophizing], and told her I did not feel okay. Without hesitation, she asked her teacher if she could go to the bathroom and came outside to find me. She calmed me down enough for us to both go back inside and contacted my mom. Bunny was nonjudgmental, cared deeply, and wanted to reduce my anxiety.

Thirty minutes later, in the locker room right before the team was supposed to get on the bus for our track meet, I broke down again. While I don't remember exactly what I said because I was in a highly emotional state, I know Sarah also saw me in a moment when I was not okay. To my surprise, Sarah wasn't upset with me either. Instead, she listened and gave me a hug. In that moment, all I needed was someone— another human being—to physically be there with me. She didn't need to try to fix or solve my pain. I just needed to feel seen, which is exactly what Sarah did in that moment. By the time we got to the track meet, my emotions quieted, I pulled it together, and I ran my events: 300-meter hurdles, 100-meter hurdles, and the 100-meter sprint. This is what mental health struggles can look like for a high schooler: you saw me doing hurdles at track, but you didn't see the hurdles in my mind I had just overcome an hour before.

On this day, the "*you are a burden*" voice didn't have a comeback. Friends had seen me in a state of suffering, and they didn't hate me or cut me off or judge me. Rather, they were incredibly supportive. Bunny and Sarah, as well other close friends whom I had begun to let in more by the end of senior year, wrote a slightly different message in my yearbook:

"*There will be 391 miles between us while we are at school next year, but that's only a phone call away...nothing can change the love we have for each other*" ~Bunny

"*Emily Freaking Kumpf...We know each other so well and can always talk to each other when we need it...Two big things I want you to remember: 1) Be yourself 2) call me–anytime. I love you X10000*" ~Sarey

Even though they had seen me in my rawest moments, my friends were still present and there as a support if I needed them. I took their words to heart and learned moving forward that even when the pain feels unbearable, there are *always* people (e.g., friends, hotline numbers, therapists, parents) you can contact.

IT IS OKAY TO NOT BE OKAY: REACH OUT FOR HELP.
Entering college, I placed all my "moments" from high school in a box, closed it shut, and shoved it into the very back of my mind. If I didn't think about my experiences from high school and told myself it was all in the past, I could prevent future pain, right?

You may have guessed that this approach—completely blocking out my past—was less than helpful. My sophomore and junior years of college, there were multiple things life threw at me that were difficult to process alone. I wasn't prepared, felt myself slipping, and began to spiral.

The difference from high school was that this time, I understood that it's okay to not always put up a front. I ripped off "my mask" and threw it into a corner of my room. In other words, I talked to people on the harder days. Calling a friend, my boyfriend at the time, or my mom didn't automatically equate me to being burdensome. Connecting to another person really helped. They were incredibly supportive by being fully present and listening, even if they didn't understand exactly what I was going through. That being said, they weren't trained professionals. It is important to note that having success with treatment in high school didn't preclude the need for a return to treatment in college. On the phone calls with my mom, she encouraged me to go back to long-term counseling. In moments of pain, I sometimes agreed with her, but when the moments passed, I again felt like I *should* manage on my own.

Junior year, I learned that sometimes, in addition to my own voice, it's important to also listen to the voices of those who care about me. Reality hit when concern extended beyond my mom's voice. My friend Isa knocked on my door at the beginning of the semester and said, "*Em, you need to go to therapy this semester. If it's too hard to think of going for yourself, think of going for me. I am worried about you.*" Her honesty and genuine care allowed me to accept that I needed help and gain the courage to reach out to Joanna—the psychologist who transformed my life, supported me through my second half of college, wrote the foreword of this book, and taught me that I can allow the beach ball to float on the surface of the water.

MOVING FORWARD

SONG: "RAINBOW"

ARTIST: KESHA

As a college student, when people asked what I wanted to do after graduation, I'd tell them about my dream to enter into the field of suicide prevention for children and adolescents. Their eyes would often widen, appearing surprised that my response was not the typical "engineering, medicine, business" answer that most other students at my university gave.

Small talk becomes deep quickly when you tell people your career goals are in youth suicide prevention. Sometimes I say mental health instead of suicide prevention, and if someone at a coffee shop asks me what I am writing about, I lead with "It's heavy. Are you sure you want to know?" before proceeding. (*Did you catch that I no longer avoid and now really enjoy coffee shops?* ☺). People frequently respond by opening up about their own or their loved one's lived experience. Several people have disclosed their own attempt history to me in coffee shops. The other day, someone shared about their younger brother and another person showed me their tattoo from the sister they lost to suicide.

Most of the time, people do have a reaction. Sometimes, people ask if I believe suicide is preventable. I have been asked why someone so "happy" would have a desire to work in suicide. Depending on the interaction and if I choose to engage, we often end up having a conversation or educational discussion about suicide. In these conversations, I tend to point to the evidence-based research about suicide prevention and what we do know versus what we don't know about warning signs, risk factors, and protective factors for youth.

However, there is another reason, not based in research, why I believe suicide is preventable: I am here.

There are also others close to me who have had suicidal ideation, plans, and attempts who are alive after getting support. Encouraging friends to seek treatment can be difficult. When friends on campus or loved ones in my life have slipped into hopelessness, I learned that while I could listen, validate, and provide resources, I still wasn't a trained professional. You cannot force another person to go to therapy. However, you can express your concern, genuinely listen, and communicate that no matter how alone the person may feel, they are never ever alone.

There are thousands of students around the country who each have their own story. These diverse stories are reflected in the hundreds of distinct risk or protect factors that have emerged in suicide research over the past fifty years. My experience is one experience, not to be generalized to every person's relationship to suicide.

My story is still unfolding. Protecting my mental health includes acceptance, seeking support when I need it, and being authentic with the people in my life (who would laugh and tell you that I am absolutely *not* the "most collected" person they know). It also includes trusting that when pain and anxiety come, they won't last forever.

CHAPTER 14:

RECOVERY AND HEALING

SONG: "SYNCOPATED HEALING"

ARTIST: TWIDDLE

Evidenced-based treatment works. Recovery is not always linear, it's often one step back for every two steps forward. Treatment is really hard work, sometimes frustrating, can take multiple providers, and include misdiagnoses. And believe me—I still have my challenging days. But I am here. I am here, and I am functioning in everyday life.

Before therapy, during my darkest moments, it was incredibly difficult for me to see the beauty in our world. I had one overarching need: push down mental health struggles, fight suicidal moments of hopelessness, and prove to both the world and myself that I was ok. When I first started therapy I listed as one of my goals: to live life without killing myself. Flashing forward in time, I have many value-based goals for my life. And I have hope.

I think it is important to acknowledge that I am very fortunate that I could access the treatment that saved my life.

Not all students are born into a family that is both 1) open to mental health treatment for their children and 2) able to afford the cost of evidenced-based and quality treatment. I had fewer barriers to treatment, and it was *still* a huge undertaking. We need to do better in our country—but writing about that will be another book later on.

WHAT DOES RECOVERY LOOK LIKE FOR A STUDENT ON CAMPUS?
Each student who is healing would probably have a different response. This is my answer:

Recovery is leaving the library to go sit on the dock by the river, allowing myself to take time to watch the driftwood and the ducks glide by.

Recovery is sitting outside my dorm against a tree in the middle of the winter, squeezing snow in between my hands instead of cutting.

Recovery is throwing on my running sneakers, and being one with the outside world during a run.

Recovery is looking down at my left wrist to see the bracelet that Bunny gave me, and remembering I am not alone in this.

Recovery is choosing to eat dinner with friends in the dining hall, rather than isolating myself for meals.

Recovery is reaching out for support on my harder days, and being there for friends on their harder days.

Recovery is following my values and dedicating time to community service.

Recovery is starting over again if a slip occurs.

Recovery is blasting music and scream-singing in the car to release stress.

Recovery is unfollowing "healthy" fitness accounts, deleting Instagram, and deleting Snapchat.

Recovery is celebrating anniversary dates of being abstinent from self-destructive behaviors.

Recovery is allowing others close to me to see *all* of my emotions.

Recovery is validating myself and my emotional experiences.

Recovery is shifting from self-hatred toward self-compassion.

Recovery is learning to say no.

Recovery is allowing mental health to be one piece of my identity, while recognizing that it is not my whole identity.

Recovery is recognizing that taking psychiatric medication doesn't mean there is something inherently wrong with who I am.

Recovery is freeing my mind—letting go of the image of how I *should* think/feel/exist in the world, and instead learning to be my full authentic self in a space.

Recovery is incredibly challenging.

Recovery is incredibly rewarding.

LIVING IN THE PRESENT AND ACCEPTANCE

SONG: "LIVING"

ARTIST: DIERKS BENTLEY

To be alive, living fully present in a moment, is a beautiful experience. Our world is beautiful. There is pain *and* there is beauty. Throughout life, beauty sometimes becomes clouded, especially in the painful moments. My mom used an analogy to explain this concept to me when I was younger. She would tell me to hold up my hand in the shape of a fist. "*Emily, imagine you are your hand,*" she would say as she wrapped a sock over my hand. "*Your worry brain is the sock, covering and preventing you from accessing your true self. Beauty right now is hard to see.*" With therapy and treatment, I learned how to reposition and change my relationship to "the sock," which ultimately led to decreased suffering.

There is an equation in dialectical behavioral therapy (DBT) that is often used to describe suffering.[187]

Pain + non-acceptance = suffering (amplifying the pain)

---

187 Linehan, "*DBT Skills Training,*" 342.

Pain + acceptance = pain

The key here is acceptance. Growing up, the less I accepted my painful thoughts or emotions, the more space they took up, and the more I lived in a constant state of suffering. As I got further along in treatment throughout high school and college, I would experience anger toward myself for not being as far along in treatment as I *should* be. Why did I still have intrusive thoughts? Why did I have racing thoughts? Why were restaurants still hard to go to without having an anxiety attack afterward? Why did I still have urges to engage in self-destructive behaviors? This stage of non-acceptance only led to increased suffering. Acceptance has involved accepting that I live with OCD. I am in recovery from an eating disorder. I have a history with self-injurious thoughts and behaviors.

Intense thoughts, feelings, urges, and physiological mental health symptoms will most likely continue to pop up from time to time throughout my life, especially during moments of stress or life transitions. It's the way my brain is biologically wired, as a person with higher emotional sensitivities, and the initial way that I learned how to react to things life will inevitably throw my way.

The difference now is that through treatment, I have learned skills to manage my reaction to thoughts, feelings, body sensations, and life events. Research demonstrates that the more you can learn to accept thoughts as separate from yourself, the more the emotional intensity of the thoughts decreases over time. [188]

---

188 Glasofer, "Five Ways to Defuse."

Mental illness or depression is often compared to being in a hole. Sometimes you try to escape the hole using a shovel (ineffective behaviors), but that only leaves you in a deeper hole. Really, what you need is someone to hand you a ladder (effective skills). *You* still need to be the one to climb the ladder, but you need to first fully accept you are in the hole. Living in a state of "I'm fine. It's fine. Everything is fine," serves a function in the short term, but is detrimental in the long term.

I mention throughout this part of the book that there are specific skills that have helped me in recovery. Some of these skills include mindfulness, self-validation, thought-defusion, healthy replacement coping skills for self-destructive behaviors, acceptance, journaling, grounding, connecting to my values, meditation, and self-compassion. Explaining all these skills would be yet another book, and thankfully, there are resources that explain in-depth how to use these therapeutic techniques.

We are all grasping for meaning and peace, which come to different people in different ways. Some people—like me— find solace in meaningful relationships, in art or music, in spirituality, in movement, or in nature.

Common humanity is one of the three principles of self-compassion that touches on the idea that we are all connected.[189] Often when experiencing a crisis, we feel as though we are the only ones on the planet who have had these experiences. Common humanity helps to recognize that we are all navigating the challenges of life itself.

---

189 Kneff, "Definition and Three Elements of Self-Compassion."

CHAPTER 15:

PAINTING THE FULL PICTURE

SONG: "CALMA" (ALICIA REMIX)

ARTIST: PEDRO CAPÓ, ALICIA KEYS, AND FARRUKO

This section has so far focused on some of my more challenging mental health experiences as a child, teenager, and young adult. Just like the entry from my elementary school journal, in which happiness and worry coexisted, there was both pain and joy throughout all of these time periods. I think it's important to mention, in an effort to continue to break the stereotypical image of mental illness, that even though all of my intense pain was real, it was just one angle of the story.

On social media, it is common for students to showcase their "highlight reel" snapshot experiences and leave out the messy, imperfect realities of life. In this past chapter, I have basically done the opposite. I talked about my struggles, without mentioning my authentic, "highlight reel" experiences or my identity outside of my diagnoses. Despite there being extremely difficult and painful moments, I too had the "best four years of my life" and "every-day college student" moments. I now want to take a minute to paint a fuller picture in order to provide a glimpse into my college experience and a true sense of who I am outside of my mental health issues. If you don't have an interest in reading this chapter, feel free to jump ahead.

Each aspect of my life listed below has a quote pulled from my old social media accounts followed by moments that first came to my mind as I was writing this chapter.

MEANINGFUL RELATIONSHIPS

"Incredibly thankful for these amazing people who encouraged me take a break from working this week to enjoy the end of senior year. Through all the beautiful highs and the dark lows of the past four years, I have been so lucky to have such an incredible support system. T-3 days until graduation. It's happening!!!" ~May 2019 (senior year)

- Snagging $20 tickets to a concert, standing in the front row of a small venue, and asking the lead singer afterward: "Why are you called the Plain White T's?"

- Late-night freshman year deep conversations with my roommate Maddie, who fully accepted the fact that my side of the room would never be clean (this didn't prevent her from living with me again sophomore through senior year ☺).

- Feeling butterflies going into the city on a romantic first date with Mir (he was a junior *and* he was taking me to a candlelit dinner—freshman year me was in total shock).

- Beaming with pride a little over a year later as Mir walked across the stage to receive his chemical engineering degree—as an international student from Central America, he had achieved his dream of graduating from a university in the United States.

- Climbing trees, nature walks, and stargazing on the roof with Stacey, talking about how we had no idea what we wanted to do with our lives after college.

- Going with Isa to the Chimney Bluffs, hiking up to the top, and starring out into the space where the sea meets the sky.

- Walking into my off-campus house to a surprise party that my friends threw for my twenty-first birthday (homemade birthday cake *and* a pitcher of homemade sangria!),

- Smiling with joy as I watched Jordan, my close friend from study abroad, get married in the most beautiful wood barn in Texas.

- Momentarily forgetting about my to-do list while spinning, laughing, and dancing (sometimes in the rain) with Mir in the parking lot on the edge of campus.

- Discovering the beautiful taste of butternut squash pie at Chabad dinners over deep conversations with new friends.

- Philosophical conversations in the library with Rachel A. about if squirrels have thoughts. And if squirrels do have thoughts, do they also like to watch the sunset?

- Laughing with Isa as we revealed our first impressions of each other from freshman orientation week of when I knocked on her door (me: "wow, I wonder why she's so stressed"; Isa: "wow, this girl has a ton of energy").

LOVE OF EXPLORATION
(Entering college, I'd never had a passport. Once in college, I secured several jobs and was able to save up money for a newfound love of travel.)

"Easily one of the best days of my life. I walked for 3 hours touring the city, then I ran 9.5 miles around the roman ruins/ river, and then I treated myself out to a nice dinner and more gelato :) I'm happy—traveling by yourself is a high on life, inde-scribable sort of feeling."

~SUMMER 2017

- Snorkeling with a sea turtle, riding ATVs on the beach, and sipping out of coconuts while visiting Marial's home in Cozumel, Mexico, with Isa, Rachel, and Maddie

- Exploring Andalusia in southern Spain with Jordan during summer studying abroad in Sevilla, and putting my Spanish minor into practice ☺.

- Spontaneously signing up for a night tour to see the caves in Granada, and meeting new people from both Mexico and Australia. We all decided to grab dinner afterward at a local restaurant and bonded over the beauty of Granada.

- Solo weekend trip from Spain to Italy. I had my Lizzie McGuire moment—closed my eyes, made a wish, and threw a coin behind me into the Trevi Fountain (*No, I can't tell you if the wish came true or not* ☺).

- Walking around the streets of Dublin with high school friends, and experienced joy while hiking in the mountains and attending a rugby game with Bunny.

- Solo nature hike in Ireland along the Bray Head Cliff Walk where I crossed paths with another twenty-year-old. He was from Germany, and we spent a few hours finishing our hike together and talking about the beauty of life.

STUDENTS HELPING HONDURAS (SHH)

"It's really hard to put my experience with SHH into words... SHH opened my eyes up to a lot of the gang violence and poverty in central america, specifically in Honduras. But as much as it was a shock, the organization also gave me hope. Hope to change the course of a child's life, through education and opportunities."

~SPRING 2016 (FRESHMAN YEAR)

- Coffee with Jenny after the activities fair, listening in admiration as she described the mission and the work of SHH—working **with** community members in Honduras.

- Running around the soccer field in Villa Soleada, Honduras, and laughing, playing tag, and chasing chickens with some of the most inspiring kids in this world.

- Feeling at peace, sitting on the bus next to Julian and staring out the window at Honduran mountains.

- Embracing the mission as president of our university's chapter, and feeling proud when over one hundred people came to our annual fundraising dinner.

- Teaching third and fourth graders at the Villa Soleada Bilingual School for the two-week summer enrichment program, and meeting other students from universities across the United States who also cared passionately about promoting education and alleviating poverty/violence.

- Discovering that pickaxing is my favorite part of helping in the manual labor construction of building a school.

- Eating baleadas and pastelitos de piña (*Honduran foods that are so good*).

- Maintaining meaningful relationships made through SHH.

THE ATHLETE IN ME

"When I run, I am free...only me and the world. I am one with what is around me. Our earth appears beautiful. School, work, clubs—nothing matters. It is just me and the world."

~DECEMBER 2018 (SENIOR YEAR)

- Feeling empowered on the soccer field during our women's club games—a feeling of freedom that soccer has given me since preschool.

- Crossing the finish line of a half marathon in the pouring rain, exhilarated by my personal record time, and even more excited to see my friends cheering at the end.

- Doing a headstand for the first time in a hot yoga class before unintentionally somersaulting off my mat.

- Leaving my bookbag with Mir in the library, telling him "I'll be back soonish," and then spontaneously deciding a couple miles into my run that it was the perfect day for a half-marathon (*I like to run halfs, but I've never run a full marathon—it's on my bucket list*).

- Climbing for the first time with Marial, and subsequently being sore for the following week (*climbing is hard!*).

GREEK LIFE

"In high school when deciding where to go to college...I actually intentionally chose a school that wasn't overpowered by Greek life. Which is ironic...the people who I have met through Chi O

have given me unconditional love and support...it's amazing knowing there are people who would come at any time of the night when you need them."

~FALL 2017 (JUNIOR YEAR).

- Rushing between recruitment rooms and noticing my thoughts: "*Wow, there are a lot of people chanting and singing songs about their sororities...*"

- Two weeks later, opening my dorm room to discover that my "big sister" Shoshi had decorated and filled my room with balloons, streamers, and my favorite common market snack (*almonds and m&m's—I highly recommend this combo*).

- A year later, almost dropping my phone in the toilet when I got the message that my "little sister" would be Rachel G.—if you met Rachel, you would know why I was so excited.

- Sitting on Shoshi's bed—sometimes laughing, sometimes crying—debriefing our days.

- Dancing, taking pictures in the snow, and successfully wearing converse underneath my long dresses (*NOT heels*) for fraternity and sorority formals.

- Coffee, froyo, bubble tea, and study dates with other people in Chi O at my school who shared similar values of genuineness, friendship, community service, passion, respect, compassion, and drive.

- Philanthropy events each semester to raise money for the Make-A-Wish Foundation.

- Feeling emotional and proud watching Rachel give her speech as president to the class of 2020 (virtually) for their graduation—a speech filled with honesty, resilience, and hope.

FUN FAMILY HIGHLIGHTS
(as a daughter, sister, granddaughter, niece, and cousin)

"Feeling very thankful to have such an amazing listener/role model/advocate/support/passionate person in my life—mom—thank you for everything♥"

~SPRING 2017 (SOPHOMORE YEAR)

- Skydiving with my dad right before the start of orientation week, and seeing the beauty of our world while flying at about 120 miles per hour through the air.

- Returning home for the summer after a whirlwind freshman year, finally able to hug my two golden retrievers who greeted me with cries of joy and voracious tail wagging.

- Laughing with cousins as we got drenched by the mist of the waterfall at Niagara Falls.

- Feeling so much gratitude for having my brother in my life while getting similar tattoos together during Thanksgiving break in New Hope. I got a tattoo of a small dinosaur. He got a tattoo of a large dinosaur eating a toaster (*remember when I mentioned in the dedication that my younger brother is his authentic self—this is an example*).

- Reflective conversations and meaningful time spent with my grandparents.

- Early morning phone chats with my mom while walking to campus.

- Waking up early to watch the sun rise over the ocean with Deedee, stargazing wrapped in blankets, and ice cream trips with younger cousins up the Rehoboth Beach boardwalk.

- Continuing to freeze during our yearly cousin polar plunge tradition of jumping in the ocean over Easter weekend, followed by Aunt Amy's (*amazing*) buffalo chicken dip.

'JUST ME' MOMENTS WITH A BIT OF SELF DISCOVERY
SONG: "I LOVE ME"
ARTIST: **DEMI LOVATO**

Dear sixth grade Emily,

I wish I could tell you that you weren't still taking selfies as a form of procrastination during finals week. But ten years later, that's still very much the reality. However, I do have an update! You no longer hate the selfies that you've taken. You no longer tear apart every piece of yourself. You've learned to love your slightly crooked nose and your different colored eyes. You still have a long way to go. But the road ahead is one filled with love—one where you don't destroy your body, and one full of hope.

Yours truly,

sixteenth grade Emily (senior year)

- Enthusiastically throwing my entire self into new clubs and activities (*there are so many cool things to be involved in on a college campus*).

- Peaceful moments feeling the sun on my face while sitting by the river.

- Trying to warm up my bowl of pasta in the fridge. Didn't realize it wasn't the microwave until after I closed the door and started to push a nonexistent start timer button (*it had definitely reached that point in the semester—a.k.a. I needed more sleep* ☺).

- As a freshman, I listened in awe as five upperclassmen openly spoke to our incoming 2019 class about their identities. It was the first time I'd ever heard students openly self-disclose the various strengths and challenges associated with their intersecting identities. As a senior, I now stood on that same stage. I spoke to the incoming students of the Class of 2022 about my intersecting identities, including my lived experiences with mental illness, treatment, and recovery. It was one of the most honest, freeing, scary, and best days of my life.

- Defending my thesis, presenting my community-engagement capstone, and submitting my final paper of college (*a truly indescribable feeling*).

- Walking down the aisle in my cap and gown (sneaking a coffee mug underneath my sleeve), feeling gratitude as I saw close friends and family smiling—all had traveled to celebrate graduation weekend with me.

Attending college is a privilege, and I feel so incredibly thankful for all of the experiences that my school and the people there added to my life. I'm hopeful that sharing these memories will allow for an awareness that although sometimes we may think we know someone's full picture, the reality is that there are always more angles to the story.

CHAPTER 16:

MY PERSONAL WHY

SONG: "MY BROTHER"

ARTIST: MISTERWIVES

Why am I writing a book about suicide and mental health for college students? Why am I entering into the field of public health and psychology?

I desperately wish I could tiptoe around the fact that I'm in recovery from mental illness. It would be a lot easier. It would be easier to remain silent—to wait until after graduate school when it is "safer" to disclose my lived experiences. But I can't do that. I cannot wait to use my voice.

I remember my younger self, unable to speak up while in a deep state of suffering; Cathy's son, Zander; my friends breaking down; family members who have been hospitalized for mental health issues; my ex-boyfriend (Mir) who almost died; the students crying in the library; the "do or die" mentality; the students blacking out and using drugs or alcohol to escape reality; the students who see self-harm as their only coping mechanism; the students who attempt suicide; the students who die by suicide; the overworked mental health professionals; the fact that there was a counseling center director who died by suicide during the writing of this book; the majority of college administrators who don't know how to respond to a growing crisis that will only continue to worsen...

... if we remain silent.

I wrote this book because I want other kids, who *may or may not* have had experiences similar to mine, to never have to go through the hell of mental health issues alone. I want other kids to know that it's okay to not be okay. I want other kids to know that they can take off the mask—even if the mask is glued tight—and begin to peel it back inch by inch, person by person. I want other kids to know that there are resources, there is help, and that it's okay to talk and to have open conversations about mental health. I want kids to know that we *all* have mental health, as a function of being living, breathing humans.

I wrote this book because I want high school educators to openly discuss mental health, teach coping skills, offer guidance on how to help friend, and provide psychoeducation earlier as a means of primary prevention. I absolutely loved my elementary school, my middle school, and my high school, but in my twelve years in the school district, I never once had any psychoeducation from my school about suicide. DARE to resist alcohol and drugs? Yes. Driver's ed? Yes. Sexual health education? Yes. Mental health, mental illness, or suicide? Not touched upon even once.

I have written this book because I want colleges to take action—detailed action—which you will read about at the end of the book.

I wrote this book because I want to break down barriers and stereotypes for young people with lived experience who are entering the clinical psychology field. I don't want other college students to be told that talking about mental health openly is the "kiss of death" for their career. I want my graduate school application to be taken seriously, as opposed to marked in red ink as "Emily self-disclosed her 'personal why,'" tossed in a pile, and not considered further—as was described to me by a clinical psychology PhD candidate who works on reviewing graduate school applications. I do 100 percent agree that you definitely shouldn't enter the field of psychology to "figure yourself out." But if you are in recovery and stable—what if your lived experiences could maybe even be viewed as an asset?

I want *all* people to see that lived experiences shouldn't be a determining factor in assessing how effective a candidate may be for college or graduate school or employment—regardless of which field they are entering. I am hopeful for a world where there is no "us and them," where we are *all* human beings, trying our bests to navigate the challenges of life itself.

OPPOSITE ACTION TO FEAR

SONG: "I AM THE FIRE"

ARTIST: HALESTORM

Sometimes you can truly know in your heart what you feel passionately about doing, but fear prevents you from doing it.

At times, my mind screams to stay silent: *"Don't upset anyone; everyone will be mad/hate you; you will hurt/harm someone if you say the wrong thing; you won't get into graduate school; your career is going to end after people read this."* OCD broadcasts over and over and over and over and over and over.

As you read earlier, my power lies in challenging my OCD.

There is a skill in DBT called opposite action which says to "act opposite" to your intense emotion.[190] Whatever it is that your emotional urges are telling you to do, instead engage in behaviors that are 100 percent opposite and do the very thing that is in line with your values. Don't do it half-heartedly. Do it *fully.*

My colleague refers to opposite action as the "just do it" skill. For example, if shame and depression are telling you to stay in bed, act opposite: pull off the covers, get dressed, and leave your bedroom. If social anxiety is telling you to stay home, act opposite: attend the gathering, look up from your phone, and talk to as many people as you can. If fear, shame, and guilt are telling you to remain silent, act opposite: fight and advocate for what you believe in.

Typically, opposite action is used for unjustified emotions. I recognize to some extent that my fears are justified. There is stigma around self-disclosure, especially in the mental health field. Every fear-ridden bone in my body told me not to write this section. Opposite action was the skill that I used to speak my truth.

---

190 Marsha Linehan, "DBT Skills Training."

SELF-DISCLOSURE CAVEAT

"If you're a tulip, don't try to be a rose. Go find a tulip garden. All of my clients are tulips, and they're trying to be roses. It doesn't work. They drive themselves crazy trying, I recognize that some people don't have the skills to plant the garden they need. But everybody can learn how to garden," Marsha Linehan wrote in *Building a Life Worth Living: A Memoir.*[191] Marsha is a clinician and researcher who is open about her lived experience. She is the creator of dialectical behavioral therapy (DBT), the evidenced-based treatment developed to help those who are struggling with self-injurious thoughts and behaviors and severe emotion dysregulation.[192]

In a clinical setting, I learned through DBT training and my mentors that self-disclosure really needs to be used carefully and only be done 1) if you think it is in the best interest of sharing for the patient and 2) the issue is resolved.

Through all my treatment, the therapist I had one of the deepest connections with was the one who opened up to me that she struggled with OCD during adolescence. Her openness helped me immensely. I knew that she *really* understood how it felt to have obsessions and compulsions.

The caveat here is that self-disclosure in clinical work is not always helpful or effective. I'll give an example. The therapist who I clicked the least with in my life was a woman who talked for thirty minutes about herself and her own experiences. She spent most of the session explaining the brain-gut

---

191   Linehan, "Building a Life Worth Living."

192   Ibid.

connection, while emphasizing the importance of eating 0% fat yogurt to help combat disordered eating.

There is a time and place for self-disclosure. For me, that time and place is the "Personal Experience" section. Writing about my lived experiences is guided by my values of being authentic, being transparent, and being a mental health advocate.

PART V:

STUDENT VOICES AND A CALL TO ACTION

CHAPTER 17:

WHAT STUDENT MENTAL HEALTH ADVOCATES ARE SAYING

———

SONG: "CAN'T STOP"

ARTIST: **RED HOT CHILI PEPPERS**

It would be a disservice to write a book about suicide and mental health on college campuses without highlighting the fact that there are incredible student advocates already doing this work on campuses all across the country. As you may have inferred by now, I feel strongly that there is power in numbers and strength in student voices. I reached out to the Collegiate Mental Health Innovation Council to see if any students would be interested in sharing their voices and being interviewed for this book. The following interviews are just some of the additional student voices from across the country who have made significant changes on their campuses.

Similar to the primary interviews section with leaders in the field, I asked students the question, "What role or responsibility (if any) do you think colleges have to protect the mental health of their students and prevent suicide?" Every single student interviewed responded that colleges do have a responsibility to promote mental well-being, and that universities absolutely play a role in suicide prevention on their campuses.

SARAH PURSELL AND JESSICA ROBBINS, CLASS OF 2020 (UNIVERSITY OF ROCHESTER)

In the "Mental Health Advocacy" chapter, I spoke about the mental health task force (MHTF) my friend and I founded. When we graduated, two of the student leaders that we passed the torch to were Sarah and Jess.

Before my Board of Trustees presentation with my honors thesis findings, I asked our dean of students if they would be open to having another student perspective in the room. As a result, Sarah Pursell and the president of our Active Minds chapter were the other two undergraduate students who joined me in a room full of university leaders. Sarah shared her perspective as a Resident Advisor (RA). As an RA for first-year residents, she witnessed firsthand the decline in student mental health and experienced inadequate support around crisis situations. Freshmen rely on the support of RAs, and Sarah "worked tirelessly as a student mentor to combat a toxic college mindset—one of competing for who was the most sleep-deprived or who had the busiest schedule…Very quickly, the rigorous college pressure left most of the kids burnt out and mentally and emotionally unwell."

There was one particular crisis that stood out to her around a student who she knew was struggling, but who would downplay his experience. She reflected:

"...It all seemed to come to a boiling point. Without revealing too many details, late one night I was woken up by a frantic student concerned about this resident. By the time I got to his dorm to check in, he had locked himself in his room after a fight with a friend, and had threatened self-injurious behavior with the method locked away in the room with him. The scene of the incident was a whirlwind, with numerous staff from public safety to residential life intervening and very, very concerned residents watching the fallout as if it were a spectacle. Beyond the incident itself, in the following days, I felt little to no support from supervisors who only seemed concerned about protocol and less concerned about student safety or well-being. I was discouraged, frustrated on behalf of my resident, and felt unsupported. As someone who only wanted the best mental health resources—especially in a time of crisis—I felt like the university had failed my resident and myself."

A few months after the Board of Trustees presentation, the provost and president implemented a Mental Health and Conduct Report (i.e., a needs assessment) for our university. The report is meant to assess current services and mental health needs, compare services to universities of a similar caliber, include the student perspective, and ultimately drive change for policies and practices. Sarah reflected that being asked to share her perspective as an undergraduate student for this report was incredibly exciting. In her experience, the most challenging aspect of her mental health advocacy work is decentralization. While there are countless efforts from passionate and dedicated faculty and staff working to support student mental health, "communication and collaboration is often the downfall of effective implementation." Because of this, she has continued the work of the MHTF, a comprehensive approach to bringing together administrators, faculty, staff, AND student leaders. Sarah elaborated:

"Change in general—but specifically change in university policy—is particularly slow, and as a college student who has limited time at an institution, it can be frustrating feeling like the impact is slow-moving. Getting passionate people about mental health in a single place to discuss the barriers and potential solutions is hard enough, and sustaining that passion and dedication takes immeasurable individual tenacity from all levels, but when it does transpire, it is incredibly inspiring and humbling."

Sarah believes that "if universities are asking their students to invest in their programs in tuition upwards of hundreds of thousands of dollars, it is the university's responsibility to invest in its students." From her perspective, administrators too often focus on the economic payoff rather than the student experience, and that it is a university's responsibility to invest in its students beyond "academic output." She encourages university leaders to "understand what it's like to be a modern-day student, sacrificing mental health for an admirable GPA" and to "recognize that the prevalence of mental health concerns is more than just a number—it is a human experience." She highlighted the importance of bridging the gap between students and administration, "especially in mental health where the consequences can quite literally be life or death."

As a leader of the MHTF, Sarah engaged in numerous other projects throughout her senior year. One project that she spearheaded was a "Movember Male Mental Health" campaign. This project was a collaboration with the inter-fraternity committee and varsity athletics, in which both students and faculty identifying as male provided personal testimony in efforts to erase mental health stigma and foster a supportive community.

Sarah is not only a leader in mental health advocacy, but has also worked with high risk suicidal patients at our medical center across the street, and worked as a research assistant in the YR^2 lab. After graduation, Sarah will begin work at McLean Hospital—the top-ranked psychiatric hospital in the country.

One of the other student leaders who ran with the MHTF at the University of Rochester is Jessica Robbins. As a psychology major with a political science minor, Jess viewed mental health and suicide prevention from a unique perspective.

When Jess first arrived at college, she quickly noticed that "the students were wonderfully passionate...yet they didn't seem happy." She reflected that this issue is not unique to her friend group or our university. She described one moment in the library that stood out:

"I was sitting around a table with some friends, half-tuning out the conversations as I worked on a paper. I looked up to realize that they all had their Google Calendars open and were comparing to see which calendars were the 'most colorful,' or the most full. The conversation consisted of comments such

as 'guess I won't eat on Tuesdays this semester,' or "looks like I won't have time to sleep tonight.'"

As a leader of the MHTF, Jess poured her heart into the creation of a peer-to-peer support program. These types of programs train student leaders to be knowledgeable about resources, recognize signs of suicide or mental illness, and to be an active listener. The presence of "knowledgeable mental health advocates begins to chip away at a toxic campus culture." Jess emphasized the importance of representation in peer-to-peer programs in order to support each person's unique experiences:

"Whether it be a matter of race, religion, gender identity, major, extracurricular interests, etc., a peer support program allows for meaningful interactions between students that have diverse experiences."

Like other student leaders, Jess agreed that colleges have a "great deal of responsibility to protect the mental health of their students." For many college students, a campus becomes their home for four years. According to Jess, "If you follow this logic, every member of a university community becomes their family," and, "each member of the community plays a huge role in the campus culture that ultimately impacts a student's mental health." Shifting a campus culture could be as simple as "professors taking time during syllabus week to discuss the importance of taking care of yourself."

If Jess could communicate anything to university leaders, it would be that "mental health needs to be a priority, not just a side conversation...a student's mental health could be a matter of life or death." The most challenging part of doing this work for Jess is the complexity of mental health itself:

"As much as I would love to flick a wand in order to eliminate stigma surrounding mental health, provide sufficient care for all students, [and] shift to a [new] campus culture that does not normalize poor mental health habits...it is not that easy, and accomplishing these goals requires a campus community coming together to make this happen."

HELMI HENKIN, CLASS OF 2018 (UNIVERSITY OF ALABAMA)

The city of Palo Alto, California made national headlines as a result of two separate suicide clusters that occurred within one decade. These consecutive instances were so severe that the CDC was sent to investigate. Palo Alto is adjacent to Menlo Park, Helmi Henkin's hometown, and the entire community felt the impact of the deaths. As a high schooler, she reflected that "it was constant" grieving and coping. Helmi, a high-achieving student, shared that there was a competitive academic atmosphere among all of the local schools and "everybody [was] struggling," though student mental health issues were never talked about openly.

Stress diathesis models of suicidal behavior indicate that trauma can "precipitate suicidal behavior, even without the existence of predisposing psychological or biological characteristics."[193] Helmi relayed that her school didn't provide ade-

---

193 Van Heeringen, "Stress-Diathesis Model."

quate support to students who were coping with the trauma of frequently losing their peers to suicide in a short period of time. After many years of living with severe anxiety and panic attacks, Helmi experienced what she described as a "full-blown depression" during her senior year of high school, resulting from mounting academic pressure, trauma, and bullying. At the time, her family did not fully understand what was happening or how best to be a support.

Within her first month at the University of Alabama, in an effort to be proactive in addressing her mental health concerns, Helmi went to the counseling center. She shared her experience:

"They told me my problems were too long term...which I don't have any resentment [around]...Especially now after all the advocacy I've done, I realize how overworked and understaffed [counseling center staff] are. They are trained to help you if you are stressed about a test or homesick or sad about a breakup, but anything more than that, they don't have the capacity."

After her initial appointment with the counseling center, Helmi was referred to off-campus mental health services, but was unable to access treatment due to limited capacity. Helmi reflected that she loved her school and the opportunities it gave her to lead and excel in academics, research, and extracurriculars. At the same time, she shared, "College was a really traumatic time." Helmi is very open about her experiences with eye movement desensitization and reprocessing (EMDR) therapy, and wonders looking back how different her life would be had she been able to access treatment earlier in college. Helmi reflected on the difficulties of navigating "insufficient referrals":

"It's exhausting trying to find a good therapist or psychiatrist...and if you don't have a car or insurance, what are you going to do?"

Unfortunately, similar to her experiences in high school, there was also a suicide cluster on her college campus during her time as an undergraduate student. Motivated by these experiences, Helmi dedicated her time at college to raising awareness, sharing her story, and advocating for additional resources.

Helmi not only participated in mental health advocacy work on her own campus, but also worked at state and national levels. After serving as a Connection Support Group facilitator and Ending the Silence Program Coordinator for Tuscaloosa's chapter of the National Alliance on Mental Illness (NAMI), she was elected to NAMI Alabama's board of directors—the youngest person in the board's history. Additionally, she served on JED's Student Advisory Council, Crisis Text Line's Youth Advisory Council, and Mental Health America's inaugural Collegiate Mental Health Innovation Council while in college. Helmi is still involved with NAMI St. Louis as an Ending the Silence presenter, teaching middle and high schoolers about the signs and symptoms of mental health conditions and sharing her recovery story to break the stigma surrounding mental health issues. Currently, Helmi is pursuing a master of social work degree at the Brown School at Washington University in St. Louis to work with children and adolescents in a clinical mental health setting, specializing in trauma.

Through her lived experience, Helmi learned how essential it is for students to develop the ability to self-advocate. She elaborated that this can be frustrating "when you think these offices are supposed to give you more than what you are asking for or what you know how to ask for."

The perspective of administration and university leaders is often very different from the student perspective. Helmi's wish for schools is that they will begin to really listen to students and be more transparent about gaps in resources. She said:

"Acknowledging that there is an issue is really important. Schools are not perfect. And there are a lot of improvements that could be growth edges for the school. At WashU, [there is] a 'work until you die mindset...' Students end up having breakdowns in campus buildings and are taken away by cops."

The most challenging aspects of doing this work is the "blanket excuse of 'we don't have the funding.'" As a member of her graduate school union, Helmi has learned more about endowments and how universities decide how to allocate the money. She emphasized the importance of schools allocating funding to mental health resources:

"The counseling center deserves to be on campus. It deserves way more funding and staff...It's not like [my counseling center] didn't try to advertise their resources. But there's only

so much that they can do. I think it's important for students to realize that a lot of times…the school counseling center is trying their best."

Helmi's hope is that *all* schools will begin to recognize the importance of prioritizing student mental health and respond proactively to suicide prevention, rather than retroactively respond only during a crisis.

SHIVANI NISHAR, CLASS OF 2020 (BROWN UNIVERSITY)

SONG: "RISE UP"

ARTIST: ANDRA DAY

As a tenth grader, Shivani began mental health advocacy after several students in her school district died by suicide within a short period. In middle school, Shivani had struggled with self-harm, suicidal ideation, depression, and anxiety, and she said the suicide cluster "struck a chord."

Flashing forward a few years to her first year of college, she experienced a four-month depressive episode. Driven by her personal experiences, Shivani joined Project LETS on her campus. Project LETS provides education to students, enacts mental health policy reform, and trains students to be peer mental health advocates (PMHA) to help support students with a range of mental health concerns and needs, including active suicidal ideation (with intent, means, and plans). As a PMHA, students receive extensive training on de-escalation, crisis planning, and trauma-informed care in order to provide safe peer-to-peer care.

Shivani shared that when Project LETS attempted to collabo-rate with the university's emergency medical services (EMS), there was unfortunately pushback seemingly due to "liability." While she emphasized that there were some administrators who were willing to work with students in order to make mental health care more accessible, "these administrators were also lower in the hierarchy, meaning that those higher up in the administration, the ones who often had a final say on decisions, put up a lot of red tape that students had to try and cut through."

Shivani stressed that "this red tape is supported by the fear of 'liability,'" which, in her opinion, is more about higher education being scared of getting sued than it is about stu-dents actually being harmed. For example, PMHAs—like EMTs—operate under the Rhode Island law. She says, "I have often worked with suicidal students and students with mania and psychosis, and I have never had to forcibly trans-port someone to the hospital. Yet, EMS says that liability makes it hard to change their protocol. The end result? We have students who are physically restrained, sedated, and forcibly transported to hospitals where they are then invol-untarily held."

On the role of responsibility to protect mental health and student wellbeing, Shivani said that universities 100 per-cent have a role to protect their students. Her exact words were powerful:

"I'm going to throw the word 'liability' right back in their face here: if colleges are liable when students harm themselves or others, then they are absolutely on the hook for providing the

culturally informed and radically accessible support neces-
sary to make sure that students are safe. What colleges don't
seem to grasp is that support does not look like involuntary
hospitalizations, surveillance, or forced medical leaves—all of
which have or are currently happening [on campus]. Instead,
listen to your mentally ill students and trust them to know
what supports they need most."

Despite the red tape and barriers faced throughout her mental health work, Shivani continued to advocate. There are a few specific projects that she worked on that stand out:

- **Leave-Taking Peer Program**: For a long time, students on Leave of Absences for personal, medical, or academic reasons were taken off the student listservs and received little communication from Brown. As a result, students voiced feeling disconnected from the community. In order to combat this, as the chair of student wellness in student government, Shivani helped create a program where students on campus wrote letters and sent care packages to students off campus. She elaborated that "changing mental health policy is super important as providing educational/training materials...but also, we need to simply show each other that we are thinking of those around us and actively share love to our community, and these care packages did exactly that."

- **Disability Day of Action Town Hall**: In order to bridge the gap between administration, faculty, staff, and students, Shivani organized a panel event for students to openly discuss their experiences around stigmatized mental illnesses. From her perspective, "Brown is really good about talking about depression and anxiety...but there is a whole spectrum of experiences that are hidden away." Shivani described her peers as exceptional. While she reflected that their stories around "involuntarily hospitalizations and being turned away from faculty in need of support" were heartbreaking, the town hall created a space—a space for students to be open about their experiences in a room full of administrators who held decision-making powers to enact change.

MAGGIE SKOCH MUSSO, CLASS OF 2016 (UNIVERSITY OF NOTRE DAME)

Maggie Skoch Musso attended the University of Notre Dame for her undergraduate degree. In 2016, Maggie was honored at JED's annual gala with their Student Voice of Mental Health Award. Maggie shared with me a piece of the excerpt she wrote:

"As a sophomore, I began experiencing frequent panic attacks, the latest development in my experience with anxiety, depression, and OCD. By Labor Day, I was barely functioning, missing classes, and preoccupied with obsessions and anxieties that frequently devolved into panic. My undergraduate journey came to an abrupt halt as I decided to take a medical withdrawal from Notre Dame, and my goal of attending medical school suddenly seemed like a pipe dream. Although devastating at the time, this withdrawal opened my eyes to the state of mental health issues at Notre Dame, gave me the opportunity to dream about how I might make a difference, and provided me with the courage to enact change in my community.

"At the time of my withdrawal, students were required to withdraw for two semesters, regardless of their situation, few understood the entire process, and on-campus housing was not guaranteed upon return. After my experience, I was determined to take action and reimagine the withdrawal and readmission process, focusing on the well-being of the students. During my first year back, it was my mission to work with Student Affairs to improve the process. As a result, minimum withdrawal periods were replaced with personalized, case-by-case handling. The lengthy approval process was simplified and digitized, and readmitted students are now at the top of the list for on-campus housing."

First as president of her university's chapter of NAMI, and then as a student intern in the Division of Student Affairs, Maggie dedicated an incredible amount of time to make concrete changes on campus, including:

- Developing Irish Peace of Mind, a mental well-being awareness week including a student panel, a film screening, and a meet and greet with administrators.

- Hosting a lecture with the founder of the renowned mental health awareness organization To Write Love On Her Arms.

- Coordinating the addition of health, well-being, and emergency contact information on student ID cards.

- Completing a gap analysis of campus well-being resources in comparison to other top-twenty universities.

- Building an orientation program for readmitted students, and updating and improving department websites.

- Creating an emotional well-being information booklet to be distributed to each incoming freshman at the start of each school year.

The change she made in four years on her campus is truly incredible. In 2016, she reflected:

"My journey has been characterized by some of the best and worst experiences of my life, and all of it has been a gift. I never imagined my experience with mental illness would instill in me a profound desire to help those living with similar issues. I have uncovered my vocation and deepest passion in life; in the fall, I will achieve my pipe dream by attending the Stritch School of Medicine at Loyola University [Chicago], as I set my sights higher on pursuing a career as a psychiatrist. As my time at Notre Dame comes to an end, I am filled with gratitude as I reflect on the opportunities I have had to help improve the well-being of the Notre Dame family."

Maggie has since graduated from medical school, and is currently completing her psychiatry residency. Her passion for mental health advocacy didn't stop after undergrad. During medical school, Maggie helped to develop a peer-led wellness curriculum to educate students about the challenges of being well in medicine. The space provided opportunities for reflection and promoted virtue formation—an essential aspect for medical students, residents, and physicians, all populations at high risk for depression and suicide.

The most challenging part of student mental health advocacy for Maggie is staying patient "while engaging in sometimes slow efforts to make systemic changes." She highlights that colleges are trying to figure out how to care for students at both the individual level and the broader population level of the student body. Maggie emphasized the beauty of doing this work:

"As a student, advocating for my peers involved building relationships with administrators and taking the time to understand the perspectives of all stakeholders. While this was the most challenging aspect, it was also the most rewarding. I grew exponentially as an advocate and as a person through this work."

DR. LEAH GOODMAN, CLASS OF 2013 (UNIVERSITY OF FLORIDA)

SONG: "FIGHT SONG"

ARTIST: RACHEL PLATTEN

"Students are taught how to draw parabolas and conduct statistical analyses, but not how to foster positive mental health... Issues related to identity, LGBTQIA+ communities, disability, advocacy, and health promotion are often relegated to extracurricular interest groups. What if, instead, they were embedded into core curricula in a way that communicates an institutional priority of mental health and well-being?"

—DR. LEAH GOODMAN

Leah Goodman attended the University of Florida for college, the University of Southern California for her master's degree in occupational therapy, and the University of Illinois at Chicago for her OTD in occupational therapy. In her TEDx Talk, "How College Fails Us: Reimagining Higher Education," Leah highlights the importance of teaching students skills that promote their well-being.[194] She encourages you to pause and think about if you were taught the following skills in school:

- Asking for help
- Resolving conflict
- Self-advocacy
- Financial management and financial literacy
- Effective communication
- Stress management
- Self-soothing or self-regulation
- Vulnerability
- Resilience
- Self-awareness
- Self-compassion

Take a moment and really think about it. Were you taught these skills in primary or secondary school? I know I wasn't.

During her doctoral work, Leah created, taught, and measured the impact of "Promoting Wellbeing," a credit-bearing mental health and well-being course at the University of Illinois at Chicago. This course covers topics such as identity, intersectionality, and values. They practice effective communication and conflict management. They practice yoga,

194 TEDx, "How College Fails Us."

meditation, and self-compassion. They learn language for emotions, discuss relationships, and explore healthy boundary-setting. They reflect, connect, practice, and learn from one another, cultivating a sense of belonging. For many of the students, this is the first time they have talked about well-being and coping skills in a classroom.

Leah is now an instructor at a university and relays that "it's not unprofessional to self-disclose that you're human. And it gives students permission to be human, too." The following is Leah's perspective on the role of responsibility colleges have to protect the mental health of their students:

"Colleges are not mental health institutions, nor are they meant to be. I say that first, intentionally, to acknowledge that it is not feasible for university counseling centers to provide quality, ongoing, individualized mental health counseling to every single student on campus for the entirety of their academic career. However—and of course there was going to be a "however"—universities still maintain the responsibility of supporting the mental health and well-being of their students.

"The structure of university education normalizes—perhaps even romanticizes—imbalance, and minimizes the growing experience of distress. By not prioritizing well-being in educational settings, we are teaching young people that mental health does not matter. For the educational system to serve its mission 'to promote student achievement and preparation for global competitiveness,' it must actually prepare students for real life and ensure equity through mental health support. This requires a paradigm shift, a true change in the

priorities, services, and curricula that educational institutions provide."[195]

Her involvement to do this work is rooted in her values of equity, connection, and her personal experiences navigating undergrad and graduate school with depression. She noted that her "ability to succeed" academically and professionally—by a university's definition of success—has everything to do with [her] privilege and nothing to do with institutional support." Many other students don't have access to supportive resources. In her eyes, it's obvious: "The world is changing, our students are changing; we need to do better." She elaborated on the challenges in doing this meaningful work:

"Change is hard. Trying to make changes within a bureaucratic system that doesn't share your values? Even harder. To do this work successfully, I have had to learn a game that I have no interest in playing. I believe that there is an abundance of good intentions within the world of academia, but it is often stifled by bureaucracy. I have a fire in my belly when it comes to equitable mental health for college students; I care deeply about this work, which has fueled my continued advocacy. What I do not care for are the institutional barriers to equity, inclusion, and true progress."

JARED FENTON, CLASS OF 2017 (UNIVERSITY OF PENNSYLVANIA)

At the Higher Education Suicide Prevention Coalition Conference, I attended Jared Fenton's research presentation in

---

195   U.S. Department of Education, "About ED"

which he presented on the University of Pennsylvania's campus culture of wearing a "mask," commonly referred to by students as "Penn Face." Jared shared that this culture is "pervasive and debilitating." This culture, analogous to duck syndrome, impacts hundreds of thousands of students across the country. Two years after meeting Jared, I had the opportunity to speak more in-depth with him about some of his reflections on this topic. During his interview with me, Jared elaborated on the importance of a student-driven movement:

"I believe that it is essential that we empower students to take off 'the mask.' Nobody can take your mask off for you, AND you have the power to take off your mask."

Jared first noticed "the mask" phenomenon within his first few weeks of starting college. As a first-year student, he figured that the best way to meet new people would be to walk up to random students sitting alone in the cafeteria and ask to sit down. While the vast majority of people were very welcoming, Jared reflected that he felt like he was "talking to people's Instagram profiles" rather than the true individual.

This experience was one of three primary factors that drove him to start a movement on his campus. The second was the tragic suicide death of his classmate —Madison Holleran—a star track athlete who many described, according to Jared, "as appear[ing] 'perfect' on the outside." And the third experience was at the end of his freshman year, when Jared found one of his friends in crisis.

During his time as an undergraduate student, Jared expanded his activities beyond research. As a student in the civic scholar's program, he built on his passion for mental health promotion by founding a nonprofit. Below is the mission of the Reflect Organization:

"We believe in the power of students to transform campus culture. By hosting innovative, proactive programs that provide college students with a safe forum to engage in open and honest discussion, Reflect, a national mental wellness nonprofit with college and university chapters, is dedicated to empowering students to foster a culture of authenticity, self-love, and allyship on campus."[196]

"Why do we do community service?" Jared asked his mom as a child. His mom's response: "Because community service is like brushing your teeth—it's what you do every day because you're human." During his interview, Jared described the impact of "one caring person." Essentially, this concept says that just one person can change a life. If you have just one person in your life who is nonjudgmental, a steady presence, and believes in you to be your best self, then this can help foster resilience and break cycles of adversity. "There is no script for how to be that one caring person," Jared said. "It's how you make a person feel." Jared was transparent in saying that the most difficult part of doing this work is prioritizing his own self-care:

---

196 The Reflect Organization, "Learn."

"All I want to do is be helpful and supportive. And there is so much more that can be done. I need to remind myself...in order to be the best support that I can be to others, I need to make sure that I am in a position to deliver that care."

Throughout our conversation, Jared relayed the importance of students empowering one another to be their true selves. Universities certainly do have a critical role to play, and at the same time, he believes students are the ones who hold the key to enact change. He concluded the interview with a powerful, thought-provoking question: "If we really want to change the world, does it really serve us...to present...as this masked version of [ourselves]?"

CHAPTER 18:

CALL TO ACTION

———

NOW THAT YOU KNOW, WHAT WILL YOU DO?

At this point in the book, you've read about college campus culture, mental health, and suicide. You have learned about the complexity of these issues from leaders on the national and collegiate levels, as well as other student mental health advocates. And, if you chose, you dove into my lived experiences. Now, it's time for me to do one of my favorite things in the world: it's time for me to advocate for change.

I'm so happy that you—college and university leaders—picked up this book. It reinforces what I know to be true: that you genuinely care about the well-being of your students. Now I'd like to call on you to put that care into action. It is time to make student mental health a top priority.

As repeatedly echoed throughout the primary interviews section, it is crucial for colleges to have resources, a framework, and a comprehensive approach to mental health and suicide prevention (i.e., prevention, intervention, and post-vention). In addition, to improve the overall well-being of college students, colleges must encourage a shift in the student culture that places academics above health.

Change can be slow. However, there are things colleges can be doing right now with urgency. Listed below are "Twenty-One Things Colleges Can Do for the Mental Health of Their Students." This list is a combination of my research and insights from interviews with professionals and advocates in the field, as well as my subjective experiences as a college student and clinical fellow. It is by no means an exhaustive list, but my hope is that it can be used as a starting point.

Each college is unique, and as a result will have unique needs for mental health on campus. Show students this list. Ask them what may resonate from. Ask them what may be missing. And please respond to your students. Make changes. Allocate funding toward mental health and suicide prevention. At the end of the day, you have a unique opportunity to do something about promoting mental health and preventing suicide for your students.

College and university leaders—this is your call to action.

DEAR COLLEGES AND UNIVERSITIES,

SONG: "NOW OR NEVER"

ARTIST: **THE CAST OF HIGH SCHOOL MUSICAL**

Students are in distress. And we need your help. Below are twenty-one things that you can start doing to make a dent in the demand crisis and the mental health crisis that affects us both.

TWENTY-ONE THINGS COLLEGES CAN DO FOR
THE MENTAL HEALTH OF THEIR STUDENTS

1.) Provide psychoeducation:

At a minimum, you need to provide information about mental health and suicide prevention to all of your students at the start of each semester. As mentioned in the AFSP interview, there are places in the United States that already mandate this by law. In providing psychoeducation, please make sure that the information you provide is accurate. Accurate information is freely available online. Some websites are also provided with resources at the back of this book. Additionally, I believe psychoeducation is most powerful when you involve other student voices. Some of the main topics that are critical to focus on include:

- Warning signs of suicide
- How to talk to a friend when you notice their behavior change
- How to help a friend in distress
- How to recognize when you are in distress and when you need help (i.e., when does it cross the line from stress to distress to crisis?)
- How to talk to a friend about getting help
- How to cope with stressful life events or transitioning to college
- Resources available on campus and off campus for support
- Emphasize that there is no award for who takes care of themselves the least

- Encourage students to spend time with those who support their well-being and shift relationships in which mental health or safety is at risk

2.) Reflect the diversity of perspectives and identities of your student body:

Some students come into college well versed about mental health, either from personal experiences or from psychoeducation in high school. Other students arrive having very little information on mental health. It is necessary to take these varying levels into account when creating mental health programming.

As an international student mentor, I mentored students who came to college from a variety of different health care systems outside of the United States. A student's perspective on mental health is greatly influenced by their native health care system and the culture surrounding mental health treatment. Perspectives vary substantially based on a student's background, culture, and experiences. For psychoeducation to be effective, it will need to address the diverse needs of *all* students—which may be challenging during a one-size-fits-all thirty-minute presentation at the beginning of orientation. The staff, faculty, programming, psychoeducation, and resources that are on your campus need to reflect the diversity and identities that make up your student body.

3.) Teach coping and life skills to all incoming students:

Everyone can benefit from learning therapeutic techniques and coping skills aimed to reduce stress, regulate emotions, and increase overall well-being. As mentioned in the past chapter, many times, schools don't teach these skills to students. You—colleges and universities—have an opportunity to teach skills at a universal level. From the moment freshmen arrive, you have the opportunity to reach every single student during orientation. Incorporate the teaching of coping skills as an essential presentation during orientation.

One example of a coping skill available to teach is a distress tolerance skill called TIPP. TIPP is a crisis survival from dialectical behavioral therapy (DBT) that has been scientifically proven to send a signal to your brain's parasympathetic nervous system to calm down (e.g., decrease heart rate, increase oxygen flow, lower blood pressure, release tension).[197] When kids are in very high levels of distress (i.e., panic, urges to self-harm), this is the skill we coach:

T—temperature (e.g., ice dive, frozen washcloth to face)

I—intense exercise (e.g., jumping jacks, squats)

P—paced breathing (e.g., four-count inhale, seven-count exhale)

P—progressive muscle relaxation (e.g., tense and let go parts of your body)

TIPP is just one of many strategies available to help tolerate high levels of distress.

---

197 Dialectical Behavioral Therapy, "T10: TIPP."

In addition to orientation, it is important to reintroduce coping and life skills throughout the year. Consider training select students to be peer skills leaders. It could be a win-win: counseling centers don't have the capacity of staff to teach the skills? Train undergraduates who would most likely do it for free. Train psychology majors who are typically very eager for clinical experiences. Train RAs, who could also become peer skills leaders throughout the year. In training select students to initiate a campus-wide movement toward healthy tolerance of distress, the skills could reach more students on a broader scale (i.e., public health intervention for a public health crisis).

In addition, please consider creating a student well-being course like the course that Dr. Leah Goodman discussed in the previous chapter. Students don't always know the skills to best support themselves. You have an opportunity to teach these lifesaving skills.

4.) Distinguish between mental health <u>promotion</u> and mental health <u>treatment</u> in messaging:

Providing mental health promotion programming is an essential, helpful tool on campuses.

I worked in our Health Promotion Office, including in the area of mental health promotion, as a student employee freshman year through my graduation. I would like to share a few stress-reduction ideas that had great success on our campus:

- Keep stress balls or fidget toys available around campus
- Stick Post-it notes or a wall of inspirational quotes in the library and student union

- Drop-in meditation or yoga sessions
- Host stress-relief events (e.g., art, dance, music, yoga, food)
- Suicide prevention awareness week
- Bring therapy animals on campus

It's important to recognize that these efforts, while effective strategies for decreasing stress, should not be considered a replacement for treatment.

"Feeling anxious? Pet a dog!" universities say. While petting dogs is definitely wonderful and can be stress-reducing, it shouldn't be confused with treatment. Other self-soothe mental health promotion activities (e.g., coloring, putting on a face mask, eating dark chocolate, stress balls, meditating for ten minutes) will also not "treat" a mental health disorder.

The takeaway from this should not be to get rid of the dogs. The dogs are great. They do reduce stress for students. During these events, it was amazing to see the joy on students' faces when they were on their way into the gym and unexpectedly ran into a furry creature.

But it is crucial for people working in a college setting to distinguish between mental health promotion and mental health treatment. The message that "everything can be fixed" by mental health promotion ignores the fact that college students may need additional support for more serious issues. Mental health promotion must be accompanied by efforts to encourage help-seeking and treatment for those who need it.

5.) Be transparent about what services are not available on campus:

We know you are feeling the demand crisis. We are feeling it, too—and totally understand that not all services will be available or feasible on a campus. That said, it is imperative to communicate to students up front which services are available on campus and which services are not.

If during orientation all students are encouraged to go to the counseling center only to find out that the center does not have the capacity to support all students, this could lead to a lack of trust in the counseling center and a poor experience in seeking treatment.

It can be very difficult for some students to even set foot into the counseling center building. Imagine a student who takes a big leap, seeking treatment for the first time at college, only to be told that the counseling center has a long waitlist and that if they are able to be seen, it will only be at most for eight to ten sessions of short-term treatment. If you are transparent, it will prevent students from feeling frustrated. For students who need longer-term care and are referred off campus, there are often additional barriers such as cost and transportation. Be transparent about these barriers as well, and work with students to problem-solve and address any issues.

6.) Build a user-friendly website:

It may seem like a no-brainer to have an accessible website available for students. However, in talking to students and looking through over a hundred websites of different colleges, the reality is that these sites are often difficult to navigate. Below are things that would be helpful from a student perspective:

A) *Online ability to book a counseling center appointment.* This eases accessibility for students who may find it challenging to book an in-person appointment or make a phone call due to untreated social anxiety.

B) *Contact information for counseling center leaders.* It surprised me how many counseling center directors didn't have their email readily available on the website. This is problematic in terms of building trust and ease of communication between department heads and students.

C) *Search engine for off-campus providers.* If most cases are referred off campus, it would be helpful to have a resource for how to find such a provider. If there is any sort of data search engine in which students can plug in "specialty," "health insurance," or other specifications, that would ease accessibility immensely. My university had this tool available.

D) *Include pictures on the website.* Including pictures of counseling center staff and the space itself can increase comfort levels for students seeking treatment.

E) *Feedback Form.* For students to be able to provide feedback on their experiences.

F) *FAQ Page.*

7.) Create a coordinated team approach to leave of absence policies and return to campus policies:

It is required by the Americans with Disabilities Act for mental illnesses to be viewed and treated the same way as physical illnesses.[198] Thus, when a psychiatric emergency occurs, the school is legally bound to treat it no differently than a physical illness.

However, in many instances, as you have read throughout this book, often students can feel as though they are being "punished," "kicked off campus," or prevented from returning to campus after a psychiatric crisis. As referenced in the "Counseling Center Directors" chapter, a disconnect exists in relying on academic decision-makers instead of those with clinical expertise to determine whether a student stays on or returns to campus when they are struggling with mental health issues. Thus, a team approach is needed to coordinate recommendations from both a clinical and an academic perspective. Leave of Absence policies are incredibly complicated and inevitably will vary depending on the school, the people in leadership positions, the culture on a campus, and exact situations. That being said, your policies need to be posted clearly on your website and communicated to students and their families in the context of providing a supportive framework for leaving and returning. Supportive discussions around the Leave of Absence is essential in helping students to feel supported, rather than punished or afraid of academic consequences. Be mindful of the language on

---

198   U.S. Commission of Civil Rights. "Sharing the Dream."

Leave of Absence forms and the tone around communication of these policies.

8.) Be mindful when discussing mental health and suicide:

When designing programs, being mindful of the materials, literature, or activities on display is critical for building trust between students and campus leadership. I truly do believe that the people engaging in mental health advocacy by designing awareness events have their students' best interests at heart. However, everyone (myself included) could benefit from approaching mental health programming and discussions with increased mindfulness that these are sensitive topics.

An example of a time where increased mindfulness could have been beneficial:

during a suicide awareness event, administration staff encouraged students to spin a colorful game wheel in order to learn a "fun fact" about suicide. Yes, I fully support that we need to be increasing awareness. No, I do not believe that we need to be turning suicide into a game.

Be mindful that suicide is important to talk about *and* that it is serious.

Another example of an initiative that didn't meet the goals it set out to achieve was a pledge program in which students stopped by a table to sign a pledge of support. Creating a community of support is a really strong idea in theory. In practice, this pledge promoted further distance in identifying who may actually be suicidal and need help. It was advertised as "1 in 10 students contemplates suicide. Be one of the 9 students to support the 1." This statement assumed that everyone approaching the table did not contemplate suicide. While everyone was invited over to the table, in reality, the campaign was for the nine, not for the one.

Administrators, professors, and student organizations— before leaping directly into action—take a moment to pause, reflect on the goals of your programming, and be mindful of the ways you are carrying it out.

9.) Provide training:

Training academic advisers or leaders on campus to identify students at risk can be lifesaving. Similar to the B.E.A.R. Program outlined in Dr. Meeks's interview, there are evidenced-based gatekeeper training programs such as Question Persuade Refer (QPR) and Mental Health First Aid that can be implemented on your campus.[199] [200]

In addition, there are resources such as "You Can Help" trainings that teach students how to recognize and respond to students in distress. If you are not already a JED campus, I encourage you to become one. All JED campuses can implement "You Can Help" trainings that teach students how to recognize and respond to peers in distress. The cost to implement these trainings is minimal compared to the successful

---

199 Mental Health First Aid, "Identify. Understand. Respond."

200 QPR Institute, "Question. Persuade. Refer."

outcome and return on your investment when instituting proactive programming and resources.

Train ALL staff to recognize the warning signs of suicide, and ensure that they're aware of resources to appropriately refer students.

10.) Offer telehealth:

Offer students the ability to use telehealth online services. Telehealth can be an invaluable resource in increasing access to treatment for students who might not otherwise pursue it. Dr. Thomas Insel mentioned one telehealth resource, NEST, in his interview. Therapy Assistance Online (TAO) is another resource utilized by many colleges and universities. Research telehealth programs that would be best for your student body, and implement them.

11.) Student-to-student support:

Create spaces where students feel comfortable talking openly about mental health. These spaces could include student-led groups, such as an Active Minds chapter, a Reflect chapter, or a campus-led initiative that allows for opportunities to increase dialogue, decrease stigma, and provide a way for students to feel connected.

The research article "Population-Based Initiatives in College Mental Health: Students Helping Students to Overcome Obstacles" outlines two programs: "(1) a hospital- and community-based program, the College Mental Health Program (CMHP) at McLean Hospital, and 2) the Student Support

Network (SSN) at Worcester Polytechnic Institute."[201] The article also goes in depth about various ways that students can support other students. Listed below are examples pulled directly from the research article that can be instituted on your campuses:

- "PULSE is a student-run UHS-sponsored group of trained health and social justice advocates at the University of Michigan who are available across campus and active in residence halls and Greek houses

- Students trained as gatekeepers to health and wellness and emergency resources (e.g., QPR, SSN)

- Collegiate Recovery Programs (campus communities of students participating in recovery from addictions through peer support; sponsored by the Association of Recovery in Higher Education)

- Student-led screenings for depression, substance abuse, HIV, etc.

- Academic and Career Clubs (e.g., Africa Business Club, American Institute of Chemical Engineers, Association for Women in Science)

- Student bystanders trained to prevent bullying, racism, sexual harassment, etc.

---

201 Kirsch et al., "Population-Based Initiatives in College Mental Health."

- Student legal advisors (e.g., law students advising undergrads)

- Lesbian, Gay, Bisexual, Transgender, Questioning or Queer (LGBTQ) (e.g., student allies of LQBTQ students-including Parents, Families and Friends of Lesbians and Gays (PFLAG) Chapters; Campus Pride-a network for and by student leaders working to create safer campus environments for LGBTQ students and allies)

- Multicultural organizations (e.g., ALMA-Assisting Latinos to Maximize Achievement; Asian Pacific American Mentorship program; Black Students Associations/Alliances are student led organizations with campus-specific missions that promote pride and awareness of African-American heritage and provide support through academic and cultural programming, activism, and advocacy)

- Military (e.g. PAVE-Peer Advisors for Veteran Education Program connects incoming student veterans with student veterans already on campus to help navigate campus life; Student Veterans of America supports the postsecondary education and employment goals of veterans; VITAL-Veterans Integration to Academic Leadership at Bedford MAVeterans Hospital uses a peer model to provide health and mental health care and support successful integration of veterans into campus life)

- Faith-specific student groups (e.g., HSO's-Hillel Student Organizations-Largest Jewish campus organization in the world enriching the lives of Jewish undergrads and graduate students; CRU-formerly Campus Crusade for Christ, includes Athletes in Action; Muslim Students Association)

- Mental health-related student organizations (e.g., National Alliance for the Mentally Ill (NAMI); Active Minds; To Write Love on Her Arms; Advocates for Mental Health (AFH); Mental Health First Aid)"[202]

12.) Provide group therapy and evidenced-based skills groups:

Counseling centers can provide therapy groups centered around specific issues as an additional ongoing resource outside of the short-term therapy offered. Some examples of possible therapy groups include: addiction/recovery, body image/ eating issues, interpersonal skills, and Cognitive Behavioral Therapy skills groups (CBT).

Specifically for suicide, mood regulation, and NSSI, students could greatly benefit from the counseling center implementing evidenced-based DBT in a group setting.[203] Research has shown that DBT interventions resulted in "significantly greater decreases in suicidality, depression, number of NSSI events (if participant had self-injured), BPD criteria, and psychotropic medication use and significantly greater improvements in social adjustment."[204] At the eighteen-month follow-up, most of these treatment effects continued to be

---

202 Ibid.

203 Pistorello et al., "Dialetical Behavior Therapy (DBT) Applied," 982.

204 Ibid.

observed. At the Florida Gulf Coast University's (FGCU) Counseling and Psychological Services, a team developed an eleven-week DBT skills training group.[205] Its work "focused on adaptations of DBT specifically for college counseling centers as well as undergraduate course work designed to teach college students DBT skills through universal education."[206]

Therapy groups can offer much needed support to students. Colleges and universities need to be using the best evidenced-based practices on their campuses.

13.) Implement evidenced-based screening:

As discussed in the AFSP section with Robert Gebbia's interview, an interactive screening tool exists that colleges can use to support their students. Every single university would benefit from implementing screenings.

In addition, when students go into the health center for a medical appointment, there is an opportunity to do a different type of screening that flags students for mental health or suicide risk. If you screen a student who is actively struggling and it's the first time they are asked questions regarding their mental health, the screening could point them in the direction of available services—which may be lifesaving.

If you already have or plan to implement this screening tool as part of your campus primary care appointment, it is also incredibly important to train staff to ask these questions in a

---

205 Carla D. Chugani, "DBT for College Students."
206 Ibid.

supportive way that allows students to feel comfortable disclosing. Genuine concern and a willingness to listen creates a supportive space for students to share. I have a few personal anecdotal examples of instances when the questioning did not feel supportive.

Once at the college health center a question was posed as: "You aren't thinking about harming yourself, *right*?"

In another doctor's appointment, I was asked:

"You're not still doing [ED behavior] right?" and when I answered no, she said, "Oh, YAY! Thank goodness...You know, my husband, he really likes to eat cheesecake and then workout afterward."

The problem is—what if I *was* still engaging in that behavior? What if I *was* thinking of harming myself? The *"you're not thinking about...right"* framing of the question didn't provide a supportive space to answer if the answer were yes.

It is imperative that colleges implement evidenced-based screening questionnaires and trainings to ensure that physicians and nurse practitioners within the university system are informed on the most effective ways to get students to openly discuss their mental health to get the treatment they need.

14.) Improve media reporting guidelines and postvention after a suicide on campus:

Do NOT report methods of a suicide death. As you hopefully learned through reading this book, the gold standard for reporting suicide in the media is to remove details about the specific means or graphic details of how the person died. Learning specific methods can actually put a vulnerable individual at higher risk. Thus, the way that you respond to and report a suicide has the potential to have a very positive (increase help-seeking, increase knowledge, raise awareness) or a very negative (increase risk for other students) impact on the student body.

On the topic of postvention, recognize that students will need more support during the time following a death by suicide on campus. JED has an entire guide titled "Postvention: A Guide for Response to Suicide on College Campuses."[207] This twenty-eight-page document is FREE and has been acknowledged as a Best Practices Registry (BPR) for suicide prevention. Ideally, your campus already has a written postvention protocol that details a plan for how you would respond. If this is the case, I would still encourage you to read the JED document to learn how to be best prepared. If you do not yet have a postvention committee, I especially encourage you to read this guide.

At the same time that you do not want to sensationalize a suicide death, you also absolutely should not brush a suicide under the rug. Don't pretend like the suicide didn't happen out of fear that it may "look bad" for your college or university. It happened. And other students on campus will most likely need additional support during

---

207 A Higher Education Mental Health Alliance (HEMHA) Project, "Postvention."

this time. Be open. Listen to your students' needs. And be supportive.

15.) Encourage professors to be supportive of student well-being:

Start a BREATHE movement on campus—I'm serious. Deep breathing sends a signal to your brain that slows down your parasympathetic nervous system. Encouraging students to take a breath before a final exam, a presentation, or a written assignment may ease performance anxiety, as well as allow students to feel more supported by their professors.

In the "real world" (as college students like to say), life happens. Under most circumstances, the death of a loved one would excuse an employee from work to attend the funeral. In the college world, it wouldn't be uncommon for a professor to have nonnegotiable exam dates. Your sister is in the hospital? Still need to get that paper turned in by the deadline. Your grandma died? Still need to take the exam (*yes, this unfortunately did happen to my friend*).

Some professors are very rigid in their deadlines, which can reflect to students that the professor values academics over their well-being. Not all professors are like this, and I personally have been extremely grateful that all of mine have been very willing to make accommodations the few times I have needed to travel home for personal reasons. That being said, on behalf of all the people I know who weren't able to get deadlines moved, I would advocate that it is imperative for a university to encourage a campus culture in which professors promote student well-being and supportively accommodate for life's emergencies.

16.) Print the national suicide prevention lifeline number on student ID cards:

Add the national suicide prevention lifeline number and your school's 24/7 crisis hotline number directly on to student ID cards to increase immediate accessibility to resources.

17.) Create a mental health resource guide:

Each campus has multiple departments that aim to help students (i.e. disability office, counseling center, academic center, cultural center, etc). With so many offices, students don't always know which office or department to reach out to. Provide a guide that describes exactly where students can go for specific issues. Tailor it around the different offices that aim to promote student well-being.

18.) Campus-wide mental health studies:

It is critical to gather data in order to have a clearer understanding of student mental health issues, barriers to treatment, stigma, and perception of campus culture. Encouraging and supporting research related to these issues on your campus will allow you to better provide the best evidenced-based policies and practices on your campus, tailored to your specific student body.

Implement the Collegiate Center for Mental Health study. Or maybe even build off and implement a study similar to my thesis. No matter what, you need to be able to know what students are experiencing—both from a quantitative and a qualitative lens—in order to best support them.

19.) Use the safety planning intervention for suicide prevention:

It is your <u>responsibility</u> to use the best practices and evidence-based crisis interventions that we have available for suicide prevention. Building off of Dr. Benjamin Locke's interview, in which he discussed the importance of crisis planning, I strongly believe all colleges need to use safety plans for students who are at high risk for suicide. At the end of the book, you'll see an example of what a safety plan looks like that clinicians can use with their students. While safety planning sheets are evidenced-based, contracts in which students sign statements agreeing not to harm themselves (i.e. "no-suicide" contracts) show little evidence of being effective, and therefore should not be used.

20.) Increase funding to counseling centers, mental health, and suicide prevention:

Putting all the pressure on university counseling centers to "fix" mental health on campus ignores larger structural issues at play. If you want university counseling centers to improve student capacity and reduce burnout among staff, more funds must be allocated to the counseling centers and to mental health/suicide prevention resources. Admittedly, I am not versed in how budgeting works for a university—I have no idea how money is allocated, or what happens behind the scenes. But I do know that students pay hundreds of thousands of dollars in tuition each year to attend college. I know that you want to see students succeed. And I know that a part of student success means allocating resources, time, and money towards student well-being.

21.) Allow students to have a voice and get everyone together into one room:

Students <u>need</u> to be included in the conversation about mental health and suicide on campus. This includes conversations about policies and programming.

Discussions can take place at an open meeting or forum with students and administrators, a student advisory board, or a mental health or suicide prevention task force. As you may recall, my friend and I started a mental health task force as students. The interest is there—students just need to have an opportunity and a venue to have their voices heard. To help create a community that prioritizes mental health and suicide prevention and encourages a campus culture that promotes student well-being, we all need to be working together at the same table.

I TRUST YOU.

SONG: "DON'T LET ME DOWN"

ARTIST: THE CHAINSMOKERS (FEAT. DAYA)

Writing this call to action to you is a leap of faith. I chose to write because bringing awareness to the mental health crisis on college campuses is paramount. I am choosing to pour my heart and research into this book with the hope you will listen—and I trust you.

I trust you to do something. It can start with an open and honest conversation about mental health with your students. It can start with stepping out of your day-to-day role and looking at mental health and suicide prevention on your campus from a bird's-eye view. It can start with cultivating a sense of compassion, community, and connection. It can start with even simply smiling at one another. I trust you because I truly genuinely believe in my heart that you want what is best for students.

Students across the country are dying—not metaphorically. They are literally killing themselves. Allocate funding to prevent suicide. Make student well-being and mental health a top priority. We—students—need your support, and cannot do this work alone.

CHAPTER 19:

A LETTER TO FUTURE STUDENT MENTAL HEALTH ADVOCATES

SONG: "BRAVE"

ARTIST: SARA BAREILLES

It was just me, the four blank walls, and an unprecedented freedom. Thinking back to that moment in my dorm room during freshman orientation week, there are things I would want to tell the eager and excited eighteen-year-old. Below is a letter written from the perspective of a college senior to any college freshman who may be interested in mental health advocacy.

DEAR FIRST-YEAR COLLEGE STUDENT,

Hi! Welcome to college, that awkward time when you are kind of an adult, kind of still a kid, figuring out who you are outside of your family, learning what in your life is important to you, asking the question "Who am I?" nearly on the daily—all that fun stuff. ☺

I heard you may be thinking about mental health advocacy. That's cool! If I could go back in time, this is what I wish an upperclassman would have told me:

Use your voice.

Your voice holds more power than you think it does. Speak up about the injustices that you may see on your own campus.

You don't owe anyone your story.

How you disclose, when you disclose, who you disclose to, and what you disclose of your story is up to you and only you. You can be a mental health advocate, whether or not you have lived experience of mental health issues. You can be a mental health advocate and be open about your experiences. You can also be a mental health advocate and not be open about your experiences. Ultimately, it is *your* story—no one else's.

Challenge your assumptions.

Meet with university leadership. Deans, directors, and Board of Trustee members may have a more impressive title than you do, but at the end of the day, your voice has power.

Oftentimes, the people in these positions really do want to understand the student perspective. They may be a few decades older and out of touch with student campus culture, but they care about you.

Listen with compassion.

Each student, professor, and higher education professional has a different perspective and relationship to mental health. Be mindful, nonjudgmental, and compassionate of their experience when you interact. Unless they disclose personal experiences, you have no idea who in their lives has been impacted by suicide or mental illness.

Be curious.

Ask questions. Learn more. At times as a student, you may think you have read everything there is possibly to read about the topic of mental health and suicide on college campuses— the reality is that you don't know everything. There is always more to learn.

As you speak to people, be openminded to learning new perspectives. Often, the people you are talking to also wish they could snap their fingers and fix everything. The reality is that institutions are often decentralized and fragmented. There are things outside of one person's control, and change does not happen overnight.

You may not agree with their perspectives, but if you go into a meeting thinking that you know more than another person, they are more likely to react with a defensive stance. You may know more. You may not. Either way, be curious and listen with an understanding that these issues are complex.

Rise from the road bumps.

There will be challenges: moments when you feel defeated by people who seem to not be listening, moments at 2 a.m. in the library when you just want to scream at the top of your lungs, moments when someone tells you no, moments when you look up at the sky and you ask yourself why you're fighting so hard.

And then you remember all the people around you who are suffering. The people who may find it hard to use their voice. Fight for them. Fight for yourself. Fight for the students and the people who are no longer here.

Fully experience college.

At the same time that you doing this intense, time-consuming work, do not forget to be a college student.

Listen to the people in your life who say to take a night away from work or the library. Fully experience the moments of living in close proximity with some of the most amazing friends you're about to meet. Take time for a morning yoga class, for a movie night with roommates, for a social night out with friends, for a hike in the mountains, for a brunch at the diner down the street. Take time to be a college student.

Remember that you are not alone.

Just because you are a mental health advocate, maybe received treatment in high school, and perhaps even study psychology, doesn't mean you are immune to suffering. I know it's hard to fully accept this at times. Believe me, I wish recovery were a linear process. It's not.

There may be moments when you feel yourself starting to slip. When that happens, don't allow the thought "*I should be fully healed by now*" prevent you from getting help. Part of being an advocate means knowing when to advocate for yourself.

And at the end of the day, know that you are never alone. Reaching out to friends doesn't mean you are a burden. Starting therapy again doesn't mean there is something wrong with you. It means you are taking care of yourself—and for that, I am so proud of you.

There are other student mental health advocates, myself included, who will *always* be in your corner.

You got this dude.

Love,

Emily

RESOURCES AND REFERRALS

———

SONG: "YOU WILL BE FOUND"

ARTIST: BEN PLATT, KRISTOLYN LLOYD, WILL ROLAND, LAURA DREY-FUSS AND THE ORIGINAL BROADWAY CAST OF DEAR EVAN HANSEN

Listen to the above song if you are feeling alone. Remember that it is okay to not be okay. No matter how alone you may feel, there are always people and there is always help available.

CRISIS PHONE NUMBERS
If you are experiencing an emergency or are currently in immediate danger, dial 911 or go to your closest emergency room.

"We can all help prevent suicide. The Lifeline provides 24/7, free and confidential support for people in distress, prevention and crisis resources for you or your loved ones, and best practices for professionals."[208]

National Suicide Prevention Lifeline: 1-800-273-8255 (Note: This number may change to be three digits in the near future).

Crisis Text Line: Text HOME to 741741
https://www.crisistextline.org/

Spanish Suicide Prevention Lifeline: 1-888-628-9454

Trans Lifeline: 1-877-565-8860 (US) or 1-877-330-6366 (Canada)

Veterans Crisis Line: 1-800-273-8255 (PRESS 1)

National Sexual Assault Hotline: 1-800-656-HOPE (4673)

National Domestic Violence Hotline: 1-800-799-7233

The Trevor Project: "Leading national organization providing crisis intervention and suicide prevention services to lesbian, gay, bisexual, transgender, queer & questioning (LGBTQ) young people under 25"[209]

- TrevorLifeline: 1-866-488-7386
- TrevorChat (online chat with trained Trevor counselor): https://www.thetrevorproject.org/get-help-now/
- TrevorText (Text START to 678-678)

---

208 Suicide Prevention Lifeline.

209 The Trevor Project, "About."

ADDITIONAL RESOURCES WITH PSYCHOEDUCATION:
Active Minds: https://www.activeminds.org/

American Association of Suicidology (AAS):
https://suicidology.org/

American Foundation for Suicide Prevention (AFSP):
https://afsp.org/

Buddy Project: http://www.buddy-project.org/

BetterMynd: https://www.bettermynd.com/

International OCD Foundation:
https://iocdf.org/expert-opinions/subtypes-of-ocd/

National Alliance on Mental Illness (NAMI):
https://www.nami.org/Home

Mental Health America (MHA):
https://www.mhanational.org/life-campus

National Eating Disorder Awareness (NEDA):
https://www.nationaleatingdisorders.org/

Peace of Mind: https://peaceofmind.com/

Reporting on Suicide.org:
https://reportingonsuicide.org/recommendations/

Self-injury & Recovery Resources (SIRR):
http://www.selfinjury.bctr.cornell.edu/index.html

Suicide Awareness Voices of Education (SAVE):
https://save.org/

The Jed Foundation: https://www.jedfoundation.org/

ULifeline: http://www.ulifeline.org

FINDING EVIDENCED-BASED PROGRAMS AND PRACTICES

Suicide Prevention Resource Center (SPRC): www.sprc.org

SPRC Online Library: http://www.sprc.org/library_resources

SPRC/AFSP Best Practices Registry:
http://www.sprc.org/bpr

National Institutes of Health, Office of Disease Prevention:
https://prevention.nih.gov/research-priorities/dissemination-implementation/evidence-based-practices-programs

Substance Abuse and Mental Health Services Administration (SAMHSA) Evidenced-Based Practices Resource Center:
https://www.samhsa.gov/ebp-resource-center

Youth.gov Evidenced-Based Program Directories:
https://youth.gov/evidence-innovation/evidence-based-program-directories

THE JED FOUNDATION
Mental Health Resource Center: https://www.jedfoundation.org/mental-health-resource-center/

- "If you are worried about someone:
  - Someone I know may be at risk of suicide
  - Someone close to me has lost someone to suicide
  - My child has lost someone to suicide
  - I'm concerned about someone who may have an alcohol or substance use problem
  - I know someone who may have an eating problem
  - Someone I care about may be overwhelmed with anxiety
  - A friend of mine seems really down and may be depressed
  - I want to help someone who is struggling
  - I've offered my help to someone, but they don't want to accept it
  - I'm worried about someone, but I'm not sure if there's cause for concern"[210]

- "If you are worried about yourself:
  - I'm having thoughts of suicide
  - I've lost someone to suicide
  - I'm feeling down
  - I'm having trouble sleeping
  - I'd like some tips to manage stress and anxiety
  - I'm struggling with eating
  - I'm worried my alcohol/substance use may be problematic

---

210 The JED Foundation, "Mental Health Resource Center."

- Taking Care of Yourself and Others Following a Tragic or Traumatic Event"211
- Contact info from Zak Sander:
  - zaksandler@gmail.com,
  - join my email list,
  - watch my JED Storytellers video,
  - subscribe to my YouTube channel.

SUICIDE WARNING SIGNS

WARNING SIGN: TALK[212]

If a person talks about:

- Killing themselves
- Feeling hopeless
- Having no reason to live
- Being a burden to others
- Feeling trapped
- Unbearable pain

WARNING SIGN: BEHAVIOR[213]

Behaviors that may signal risk, especially if related to a painful event, loss, or change:

- Increased use of alcohol or drugs

---

211 Ibid.

212 American Foundation for Suicide Prevention, "Risk Factors and Warning Signs."

213 Ibid.

- Looking for a way to end their lives, such as searching online for methods
- Withdrawing from activities
- Isolating from family and friends
- Sleeping too much or too little
- Visiting or calling people to say goodbye
- Giving away prized possessions
- Aggression
- Fatigue

WARNING SIGN: MOOD[214]

People who are considering suicide often display one or more of the following moods:

- Depression
- Anxiety
- Loss of interest
- Irritability
- Humiliation/Shame
- Agitation/Anger
- Relief/Sudden Improvement

---

214 Ibid.

RECOMMENDATIONS FOR COVERING SUICIDE

AVOID	INSTEAD
Describing or depicting the method and location of the suicide.	Report the death as a suicide; keep information about the location general.
Sharing the content of a suicide note.	Report that a note was found and is under review.
Describing personal details about the person who died.	Keep the information about the person general.
Presenting suicide as a common or acceptable response to hardship.	Report that coping skills, support, and treatment work for most people who have thoughts about suicide.
Oversimplifying or speculating on the reason for the suicide.	Describe warning signs and risk factors (e.g., mental illness, relationship problems) that give suicide context.
Sensationalizing details in the headline or story.	Report on the death using facts and language that are sensitive to a grieving family.
Glamorizing or romanticizing suicide.	Provide context and facts to counter perceptions that the suicide was tied to heroism, honor, loyalty to an individual or group.
Overstating the problem of suicide by using descriptors like "epidemic" or "skyrocketing."	Research the best available data and use words like "increase" or "rise."
Prominent placements of stories related to a suicide death in print or in a newscast.	Place a print article inside the paper or magazine and later in a newscast.

Table is from: https://reportingonsuicide.org/

CHECKLIST FOR RESPONSIBLE REPORTING:

- "Report suicide as a public health issue. Including stories on hope, healing, and recovery may reduce the risk of contagion."[215]

---

215 Reportingonsuicide.org, "Recommendations."

- "Include Resources. Provide information on warning signs of suicide risk as well as hotline and treatment resources. At a minimum, include the National Suicide Prevention Lifeline and Crisis Text Line...or local crisis phone numbers."[216]

- "Use Appropriate Language. Certain phrases and words can further stigmatize suicide, spread myths, and undermine suicide prevention objectives such as 'committed suicide' or referring to suicide as 'successful,' 'unsuccessful,' or a 'failed attempt.' Instead use, 'died by suicide,'... or, 'killed him/herself.'"[217]

- "Emphasize Help and Hope. Stories of recovery through help-seeking and positive coping skills are powerful, especially when they come from people who have experienced suicide risk."[218]

- "Ask an Expert. Interview suicide prevention or mental health experts to validate your facts on suicide risk and mental illness."[219]

---

216 Ibid.

217 Ibid.

218 Ibid.

219 Ibid.

SAFETY PLAN TEMPLATE:

This template is to be utilized by clinicians with their at-risk suicidal patients.[220]

SAFETY PLAN
Step 1: Warning signs:
1. _____
2. _____
3. _____
Step 2: Internal coping strategies - Things I can do to take my mind off my problems without contacting another person:
1. _____
2. _____
3. _____
Step 3: People and social settings that provide distraction:
1. Name_____ Phone_____
2. Name_____ Phone_____
3. Place_____
4. Place_____
Step 4: People whom I can ask for help:
1. Name_____ Phone_____
2. Name_____ Phone_____
3. Name_____ Phone_____
Step 5:Professionals or agencies I can contact during a crisis:
1. Clinician Name_____ Phone_____
Clinician Pager or Emergency Contact #_____
2. Clinician Name_____ Phone_____
Clinician Pager or Emergency Contact #_____
3. Suicide Prevention Lifeline: 1-800-273-TALK (8255)
4. Local Emergency Service _____
Emergency Services Address_____
Emergency Services Phone _____
Making the environment safe:
1. _____
2. _____
From Stanley, B. & Brown, G.K. (2011). Safety planning intervention: A brief intervention to mitigate suicide risk. *Cognitive and Behavioral Practice*. 19, 256–264

Sometimes, there is an additional line added to the safety plan.[221]

---

220 Stanley and Brown, "Safety Planning Intervention."

221 Suicide Prevention Lifeline, "Patient Safety Planning Template."

The one thing that is most important to me and worth living for is: _____

ACKNOWLEDGEMENTS

"It makes such a difference," said Winnie the Pooh, "to have someone who believes in you."

I am honestly at a loss for words. To everyone who has supported me, offered words of affirmation, and encouraged me to follow my passion in writing this book—thank you.

To my immediate family, I don't even know where to start. In terms of this book: Mom, thank you for being a second set of eyes on each section, and being with me for every step of this journey. Dad, thank you for motivational texts and reminding me to channel my inner strength. Ryan, thank you for your direct feedback and your humor. In terms of everything else: Mom and Dad, thank you for encouraging me to go to counseling and for your unwavering support. Mom, thank you for introducing me to the healing power of music. Dad, thank you for taking me on my first run in second grade. Ry, thank you for nature walks and everything else—I cannot imagine having anyone else as my brother. ☺

To the two golden retrievers who always seemed to find a way to be there when the noise in my mind felt unbearable:

- Cassidy (September 2004–October 2016): second grade to sophomore year of college.

- Sophie (September 2010–May 2020): seventh grade to two weeks before copy editing.

To my support system of friends and family—you know who you are—this book wouldn't have been possible without you.

To Isabel ("Isa") Rothman, Ellen ("Bunny") Harsha, Sammir ("Mir") Antonio Lesage Quezada and all the people who have been there with me during my "moments."

To Dr. Chansky—thank you for supporting me in elementary school and teaching me about my "worry brain." Your kindness while challenging me to confront my fears helped me immensely.

To Kelly Corbitt, for being such a warm and compassionate support—thank you for introducing me to the power of mindfulness and for being there at a time in high school when I needed to feel fully seen and heard. Thank you for teaching me that no matter how alone a person may feel, they are never truly alone.

To Joanna—I sometimes wonder how different my life would be right now had I not met you my junior year of college. Would I still have pursued and published this book? Would

I have followed my passions to work at a psychiatric hospital postgraduation as a DBT skills coach for adolescents who struggle with emotion dysregulation and an ERP coach for kids battling OCD? I honestly have no idea where I would be or what I would be doing had our paths never crossed. Thank you for helping me in more ways than I can begin to express in words. Having you as a therapist, role model, and support changed my life in the best way possible.

To the teachers (K-12) and coaches at Pennsbury School District—gratitude is an understatement.

SONG: **"LIFE CHANGES"**

ARTIST: **THOMAS RHETT**

To the all the people (i.e. friends, family, coworkers—again, you know who you are) who so willingly read sections of the book early; to all the people who preordered the book and followed my publishing journey; to my Beta Readers: Grandma Elaine and Papa Steve, Dad, Carol Romano, and Barbara Mangas—thank you. To Mrs. Thomas, thank you for your never-ending support, for sharing a piece of Zander's Story, and for the Untold Foundation.

To the leaders in the field who interviewed for this book, I feel so incredibly grateful: John MacPhee, Zak Sandler, Robert Gebbia, Dr. Daniel Reidenberg, Alison Malmon, Jennifer Rothman, Kelly Davis, Dr. Rosie Phillips Davis, Patrick J. Kennedy, Dr. Thomas Insel, Dr. Daniel Eisenberg, Dr. Beth Ann Griffin, Dr. Benjamin Locke, Dr. Brigid Cahill, Dr. Will Meeks, Dr. Gregory Eells. To Michelle Eells, thank you for your kindness, warmth, support of this book, and sharing your reflections. To Sarah, Jess, Helmi, Shivani, Maggie, Leah, and Jared—thank you for sharing your perspective.

To Students Helping Honduras, Shin Fujiama, the Villa Soleada Bilingual School, and the people I have met through SHH—you give me hope.

To my mentors, advisors, supervisors, and those who were supportive of my passions at Rochester:

- Dr. Cassie Glenn and the YR² Lab (research assistants, graduate students, and lab managers)—thank you for your support in both my research and my advocacy. The basement of Meliora Hall will forever hold a special place in my heart. ☺

- Amy McDonald—thank you for reading my manuscript early, and for being a supportive person in my life during college and beyond. Linda Dudman, Arlita Gleichman, and the Health Promotion Office (HPO)—I learned so much as a meditation instructor and a program assistant for HPO. Thank you for supporting me and always listening to my perspective.

- Dr. White, Dr. Chin, Professor McNulty, and the entire public health department; Dr. Brigid Cahill and the University Counseling Center; Dean Runner and the Office of the Dean of Students; board of trustees: Student Life Committee; Dr. Jessica Guzman Rae and the Burgett Intercultural Center; Jenn Beideman and the Healthi Kids Network; Sara Scott and the Department of Recreation and Youth Services; Lauren Caruso, Professor Stu Jordan,

Mary Beth Spinelli, Glenn Cerosaletti, and the Rochester Center for Community Leadership (RCCL)—thank you.

To the residents and colleagues with whom I have had the privilege of crossing paths with at McLean hospital—you inspire me.

- To my clinical supervisor from 3East, Wendy Bamatter, thank you for your validating, empathetic, and incredibly helpful supervision—your insights were invaluable. To DBT consultation team leaders, Judy Mintz and Blaise Aguirre—thank you for providing a supportive space. To my coworkers from 3East—Rebecca Waters, Sara Brown, and Jennifer Baptiste—thank you for being role models in professionalism, advocacy, genuineness, and quality clinical care. Rebecca, thank you for everything. To Alan Fruzetti, Lucy Payne, and the research team at 3East, thank you so much for your support and mentorship.

- To my clinical supervisor from OCDI Jr., Rebecca Schneider, and program director, Maria Fraire—thank you for reading my lived experiences section of the book early and supporting me to write in my authentic voice. To Jovana Calvillo, thank you for being you and for all your encouragements. To Ryan Dresser, thank you for the inspirational quotes and unicorn gifs during the month of copyediting—I appreciate you. To the other exposure coaches at OCDI Jr., I have learned so much from you. Thank you for fostering a caring environment for both kids and staff.

To my editor, Elina Oliferovskiy, thank you for all the late-night Zoom calls, the moments when you encouraged me to keep moving forward, and for truly believing in me. To the head of publishing, Brian Bies, to Eric Koester, and to the entire New Degree Press publishing team—thank you. To Aliye Gallagher and Ryan Kumpf for inspiration for the cover design, thank you.

SONG: "FIGHTER"

ARTIST: CHRISTINA AGUILERA

And finally, I wanted to give a shout out to you—my psychiatric disorders. Ironic, isn't it? Given the amount of times that I've stared up into the sky and desperately begged the world for a different brain. At the end of the day, you challenged me at an early age to see my true inner strength. You taught me about the power of resilience. I learned through battling you: I am a full, authentic, passionate, kick-ass human. You do not define who I am at my core. I am enough just the way I am.

I'M FINE PLAYLIST:

SONG TITLE	ARTIST
"This is Me"	Keala Settle
"Before You Go"	Lewis Capaldi
"Ocean"	Lady A
"We Are Warriors"	Avril Lavigne
"Heavy"	Linkin Park feat. Kiiara
"These Memories"	Hollow Coves
"Waving Through a Window"	Dear Evan Hansen original Broadway cast
"1-800-273-8255"	Logic (feat. Alessia Cara and Khalid)
"Follow the Sun"	Xavier Rudd
"How Far I'll Go"	Auli'i Cravalho

"You've Got The Love"	Florence + The Machine
"Keep Your Head Up"	Ben Howard
"i believe"	Christina Perri
"I Am Light"	India.Arie
"Put Down What You Are Carrying"	Trevor Hall and Brett Dennen
"Where Is The Love?"	Black Eyed Peas
"One Day"	Matisyahu
"Send Them Off!"	Bastille
"Warrior"	Demi Lovato
"Simple Song"	Miley Cyrus
"i can't breathe"	Bea Miller
"My Worst Enemy"	Hailey Knox
"Beautiful Girl"	William Fitzsimmons
"Better Days"	The Goo Goo Dolls
"Tourniquet"	Evanescence
"Head Above Water"	Avril Lavigne
"Rainbow"	Kesha
"Syncopated Healing"	Twiddle
"Living"	Dierks Bentley
Calma (Alicia Remix)	Pedro Capó, Alicia Keys, and Farruko
"I Love Me"	Demi Lovato
"My Brother"	MisterWives
"I Am the Fire"	Halestorm
"Can't Stop"	Red Hot Chili Peppers
"Rise Up"	Andra Day
"Fight Song"	Rachel Platten
"Now Or Never"	cast of High School Musical
"Don't Let Me Down"	The Chainsmokers (feat. Daya)
"Brave"	Sara Bareilles
"You Will Be Found"	Ben Platt, Kristolyn Lloyd, Will Roland, Laura Dreyfus, and the original cast of Dear Evan Hansen
"Life Changes"	Thomas Rhett
"Fighter"	Christina Aguilera

BONUS go-to recovery and healing songs from my high school playlist: ☺

Song Title (Artist):

- "I Gotta Feeling" (Black Eyed Peas)
- "Hallelujah" (Panic! At The Disco)
- "Sippin' On Sunshine" (Avril Lavigne)
- "Comes And Goes (In Waves)" (Greg Laswell)
- "Survival" (Eminem)
- "Anna Sun" (WALK THE MOON)
- "Hurricane" (Halsey)
- "Ghost" (Ella Henderson)
- "The Climb" (Miley Cyrus)
- "Little Bird" (Ed Sheeran)
- "Dancing Queen" (*Mamma Mia!* The Movie Soundtrack)

It's okay not to be okay.

APPENDIX

Note from the Author
Frankl, E. Viktor. *Man's Search for Meaning*. Boston: Beacon Press, 2006.

How to Navigate This Book
National Institute of Mental Health. "Suicide." Last modified April 2019. https://www.nimh.nih.gov/health/statistics/suicide.shtml.

PART I: POST-COLLEGE REFLECTIONS

The Complexity of Suicide
Genius, "Lewis Capaldi 'Before You Go' Official Lyrics & Meaning," April 22, 2020, video, 6:56. https://www.youtube.com/watch?v=oiBTwBBUYSc.

Lady Antebellum, "Lady Antebellum - Ocean," September 20, 2020. Video, 3:34. https://www.youtube.com/watch?v=sWBqdWT-g3Vs.

Lewis Capaldi, "Before You Go (Official Video)," January 24, 2020, video, 4:06. https://www.youtube.com/watch?v=Jtauh8GcxBY.

Linehan, Marsha M. *DBT Skills Training Handouts and Worksheets.*
2nd ed. New York: Guilford Press, 2014.

Linehan, Marsha M. *DBT Skills Training Handouts and Worksheets.*
2nd ed. New York: Guilford Press, 2014.

The Ty Bentli Show, "Lady Antebellum Discusses the Passion
Behind Their New Song, 'Ocean' - The Ty Bentli Show" September 23, 2019. Video, 4:19. https://www.youtube.com/
watch?v=0ZB5Wdv5Y80.

Dr. Gregory Eells
TEDx Talks, "Cultivating Resilience | Greg Eells | TedxCortland,"
January 16, 2015, video, 15.18. https://www.youtube.com/
watch?v=eLzVJVM1BUc.

Global Pandemic
Active Minds. "The Impact of COVID-19 on Student Mental
Health." Accessed on May 20, 2020. https://www.activeminds.
org/studentsurvey/.

Ao, Bethany. "College Students Experience Mental Health Decline
From COVID-19 Effects, Survey Finds. Here's How to Get
Help." *The Philadelphia Inquirer.* May 14, 2020. https://www.
inquirer.com/health/coronavirus/covid19-coronavirus-college-students-mental-health-20200514.html.

Avril Lavigne, "We Are Warriors (Official Video)," April 30, 2020,
video, 3:47. https://www.youtube.com/watch?v=3tBk7ONm95Q.

Dennon, Anne. "Coronavirus and the Student Mental Health Crisis." *Best Colleges*. April 22, 2020. https://www.bestcolleges. com/blog/coronavirus-and-student-mental-health-crisis/.

Dwyer, Colin. "Some of the Greatest Causes of Misery: U.N. Warns of Pandemic's Mental Health Costs." *NPR*. May 14, 2020. https://www.npr.org/sections/coronavirus-live-updates/2020/05/14/855894146/some-of-the-greatest-causes-of-misery-u-n-warns-of-pandemic-s-mental-health-cost.

Gold, Jessica. "Could COVID-19 Finally Destigmatize Mental Illness?" *Time*. May 13, 2020. https://time.com/5835960/coronavirus-mental-illness-stigma/.

Gunnell, David, Louis Appleby, Ella Arensman, Keith Hawton, Ann John, Nav Kapur, et al. "Suicide Risk and Prevention During the COVID-19 Pandemic." *The Lancet 7* (6): 468 - 471. April 21, 2020. https://doi.org/10.1016/S2215-0366(20)30171-1.

Iati, Marisa and Bellware, Kim. "NYC Emergency Doctor Dies by Suicide, Underscoring a Secondary Danger of the Pandemic." *The Washington Post*. April 28, 2020. https://www. washingtonpost.com/nation/2020/04/28/nyc-doctor-lorna-breen-coronavirus/.

Jackson, Angie. "Missed Milestones, Loneliness Take a Toll on Teens' Mental Health." *Detriot Free Press*, May 17, 2020. https://www.freep.com/in-depth/news/local/michigan/detroit/2020/05/17/high-school-senior-wants-classmates-look-ways-celebrate/5195075002/.

Koons, Cynthia, Riley Griffin, and Emma Court. "The Next Covid Crisis Could Be a Wave of Suicides." *Bloomberg.* May 8, 2020. https://www.bloomberg.com/news/articles/2020-05-08/mental-health-care-braces-for-coronavirus-anxiety-and-suicides.

Noguchi, Yuki. "Act Now to Get Ahead of a Mental Health Crisis, Specialists Advise U.S." *NPR.* May 13, 2020. https://www.npr.org/sections/health-shots/2020/05/13/850665769/act-now-to-get-ahead-of-a-mental-health-crisis-specialists-advise-u-s.

PART II: A STUDENT PERSPECTIVE

Chapter 1: A Day in the Library

Plante, Chris. "This is Fine Creator Explains the Timeliness of his Meme." KC Green, May 5, 2016. https://www.theverge.com/2016/5/5/11592622/this-is-fine-meme-comic.

Tiger Sun. "Duck Syndrome and a Culture of Misery." *The Stanford Daily,* January 31, 2018. https://www.stanforddaily.com/2018/01/31/duck-syndrome-and-a-culture-of-misery/.

Chapter 2: Defining the Problem

Active Minds. "Statistics." Accessed on May 20, 2020. https://www.activeminds.org/about-mental-health/statistics/.

American Foundation for Suicide Prevention. "Ask Dr. Jill: Does Mental Illness Play a Role in Suicide?" Accessed on May 1, 2020. https://afsp.org/story/ask-dr-jill-does-mental-illness-play-a-role-in-suicide.

Auerback, R.P., Mortier, P., Bruffaerts, R. Alonso, J., Benjet, C, Cuiipers, P. "The Who World Mental Health Surveys International College Student Project: Prevalence and Distribution of mental disorders. *Journal of Abnormal Psychology*, in press, 127, (2018): 623-638. https//doi.org/10.1037/abn0000362.

Centers for Disease Control and Prevention. "Preventing Suicide." Accessed on May 1.2020. https://www.cdc.gov/violenceprevention/suicide/fastfact.html.

Cha, Christine, Peter J. Franz, Eleonora M. Guzmán, Catherine R. Glenn, Evan M. Kleiman & Matthew K. Nock. "Annual Research Review: Suicide among youth - epidemiology, (potential) etiology, and treatment." *Journal of child psychology and psychiatry, and allied disciplines, 59,* no.4 (November 2017): 460–482. https://doi.org/10.1111/jcpp.12831.

Klonsky, E. David and Alexis M. May. "The Three-Step Theory [3ST]: A New Theory of Suicide Rooted in the "Ideation-to-Action" Framework. *International Journal of Cognitive Therapy,* 8, no.2 (2015):114–129. https://doi.org/10.1521/ijct.2015.8.2.114.

National Suicide Prevention Lifeline. "Mental Health & Suicide Prevention Glossary." Accessed on May 20, 2020. https://suicidepreventionlifeline.org/mental-health-suicide-prevention-glossary/

Linehan, Marsha M. *DBT Skills Training Handouts and Worksheets.* 2nd ed. New York: Guilford Press, 2014.

Liu, Cindy et al. "The Prevalence and Predictors of Mental Health Diagnoses and Suicide Among U.S. College Students: Implications for Addressing Disparities in Service Use." *Depression and Anxiety* 36, no.1 (2019): 8 – 17. https://doi.org/10.1002/da.22830.

Nock, M.K., Prinstein, M.J., Sterba, S. "Revealing the form and function of self-injurious thoughts and behaviors: A real-time ecological assessment study among adolescents and young adults." *Journal of Abnormal Psychology* 118, no.4 (2009): 816–827.http://dx.doi.org/10.1037/a0016948.

Reilly, Katie. "Record Number of College Students are Seeking Treatment for Depression and Anxiety – But Schools Can't Keep Up." *Time.* March 18, 2018. https://time.com/5190291/anxiety-depression-college-university-students/.

Safe Colleges. "Suicide Second Highest Cause of Death Among College Students." https://www.safecolleges.com/suicide-second-highest-cause-of-death-among-college-students/

Suicide Prevention Lifeline. "Mental Health and Suicide Prevention Glossary." Accessed on May 1.2020. https://suicidepreventionlifeline.org/mental-health-suicide-prevention-glossary/

Suicide Prevention Resource Center. "Promoting Mental Health and Preventing Suicide in College and University Settings." Newton, MA: Education Development Center, Inc., 2004. https://www.sprc.org/sites/default/files/migrate/library/college_sp_whitepaper.pdf.

Van Orden, Kimberly, Tracey K. Witte, Kelly C. Cukrowicz, Scott Braithwaite, Edward A. Selby, and Thomas E. Joiner. "The

Interpersonal Theory of Suicide." *Psychological Review 117,* no.2 (2010): 575–600. https://doi.org/10.1037/a0018697.

Chapter 3: Suicide (1-800-273-8255)
American Foundation for Suicide Prevention. "Suicide Statistics." Accessed on May 1, 2020. https://afsp.org/suicide-statistics/.

American Psychological Association. "After Decades of Research, Science Is No Better Able to Predict Suicidal Behaviors. Accessed on May 1,2020. https://www.apa.org/news/press/releases/2016/11/suicidal-behaviors.

Cha, Christine, Peter J. Franz, Eleonora M. Guzmán, Catherine R. Glenn, Evan M. Kleiman & Matthew K. Nock. "Annual Research Review: Suicide among youth - epidemiology, (potential) etiology, and treatment." *Journal of child psychology and psychiatry, and allied disciplines 59,* no.4 (November 2017):460–482. https://doi.org/10.1111/jcpp.12831.

Centers for Disease Control and Prevention. "Preventing Suicide." Accessed on May 1.2020. https://www.cdc.gov/violenceprevention/suicide/fastfact.html.

Franklin, Joseph C., Jessica D. Ribeiro, Kathryn R. Fox, Kate H. Bentley, Evan M. Kleiman, Xieyining Huang, Katherine M. Musacchio, Adam C. Jaroszewski, Bernard P. Chang, and Matthew K. Nock. "Risk Factors for Suicidal Thoughts and Behaviors: A Meta-Analysis of 50 Years of Research." *Psychological Bulletin* 143, no. 2 (2017): 187–232, https://doi.org/10.1037/bul0000084.

Glenn, C.R., Lanzillo, E.C., Esposito, E.C., Santee, A.C., Nock, M.K., & Auerbach, R.P. (2017). Examining the course of suicidal and nonsuicidal self-injurious thoughts and behaviors in outpatient and inpatient adolescents. Journal of Abnormal Child Psychology 45, no.5 (2017): 971–983. https://doi. org/10.1007/s10802-016-0214-0.

Harvard Health Publishing. "Left Behind After Suicide." Harvard Medical School. Accessed on May 1, 2020. https://www.health. harvard.edu/mind-and-mood/left-behind-after-suicide.

James, Herman, S. Rankin, M. Keislin, L. Mottet and M. Anafi. "The Report of the 2015 U.S. Transgender Survey. National Center for Transgender Equality. 2016. https://www.transequality. org/sites/default/files/docs/USTS-Full-Report-FINAL.PDF

Kapil, Rubina. "How to Talk to Someone About Suicide." Mental Health First Aid. October 15, 2019. https://www.mentalhealthfirstaid.org/2019/10/how-to-talk-to-someone-about-suicide/.

Nock, M.K., Borges, G., Bromet, E., Cha, C.B., Kessler, R.C., & Lee, S. (2008). "Suicide and suicidal behavior." Epidemiologic Reviews 30, no.1 (November 2008): 133–154. https://doi. org/10.1093/epirev/mxn002.

Nock, Matthew, Green, J.G., Hwang, I., McLaughlin, K.A., Sampson, N.A., Zaslavsky, A.M., & Kessler, R.C. "Prevalence, correlates, and treatment of lifetime suicidal behavior among adolescents: Results from the National Comorbidity Survey Replication Adolescent Supplement. JAMA Psychiatry 70, no.3 (2013): 300–310. https://doi.org/10.1001/2013.jamapsychiatry.55.

Suicide Prevention Resource Center. "A Comprehensive Approach to Suicide Prevention." Accessed on May 4, 2020. https://www.sprc.org/effective-prevention/comprehensive-approach.

The Untold Foundation. "Our Story." Accessed on May 1, 2020. https://www.theuntoldfoundation.org.

Chapter 4: Research and Advocacy

Clement, S., Schauman, O, Graham, T., Maggioni, R., Evans-Lacko, S. Bezbordodovs, No, Thornicroft, G. "What is the Impact of Mental Health-Related Stigma on Help-Seeking? A Systemic Review of Quantitative and Qualitative Studies. Osychological Medicine 45, no.1 (2015):11-27. https:// DOI: 10.1017/S0033291714000129.

Corrigan, Patrick, Jonathon E. Larson, and Nicolas Rüsch. "Self-stigma and the 'why try' effect: Impact on Life Goals and Evidence-Based Practices." *World Psychiatry* 8,no.2 (2009): 75-81. https://doi.org/10.10002/j.2051-5545.2009.tb00218.x.

Fairburn, C. G., & Beglin, S. J., (1994). Assessment of eating disorder psychopathology: interview or self-report questionnaire? *International Journal of Eating Disorders* 16, no.4 (1994): 363-370. https://pubmed.ncbi.nlm.nih.gov/7866415/.

Fox Annie, Valerie A. Earnshaw, Emily C. Taverna, and Dawne Vogt. "Conceptualizing and Measuring Mental Illness Stigma: The Mental Illness Stigma Framework and Critical Review of Measures." *Stigma Health* 3, no.4 (2018):348-376. https://doi:10.1037/sah0000104

Greenstein, Luna. NAMI. "Why Suicide Reporting Guidelines Matter." Accessed on May 1, 2020. https://www.nami.org/Blogs/NAMI-Blog/June-2018/Why-Suicide-Reporting-Guidelines-Matter.

Guarneri, J. A., Oberleitner, D. E., & Connolly, S. "Perceived Stigma and Self-Stigma in

College Students: A Literature Review and Implications for Practice and Research. *"Basic*

and Applied Social Psychology, 41, no.1 (2019): 48-62. https://guilfordjournals.com/doi/pdfplus/10.1521/jscp.2006.25.8.875.

Healthy Minds Network. "Research on Adolescent and Young Adult Mental Health." Accessed on May 1, 2020. https://healthymindsnetwork.org/research/publications/.

Kessler, C. Ronald, Peggy R. Barker, Lisa J. Colpe, Joan F. Epstein, Joep C. Groerer, Eva Hiripi, Mary J. Howes, Sharon-Lise T. Normand, Ronald W. Manderscheid, Ellen E. Walters, Alan M.

Nock, K. Matthew, Elizabeth B. Holmber, Valerie I. Photos, Bethany D.Michel "Self-Injurous Thoughts and Behaviors Interview: Development, Reliability, and Validity in an Adolescent Sample. *Psychological Assessment* 19, no.3 (September 2007): 309-317. https://doi.org/10.1037/1040-3590.19.3.309.

Prins, Annabel, Michelle J. Bovin, Derek J. Smolenski, Brian P. Marx, Rachel Kimerling, Michael A. Jenkins-Guarnieri, Danny G. Kaloupek, Paula P. Schnurr, Anica Pless Kaiser, Yani E. Leyva, Quyen Q Tiet. "The Primary Care PTSD Screen for

DSM-5 [PC-PTSD-5]: Development and Evaluation within a Veteran Primary Care Sample." *Journal of General Medicine* 31, no.10 (October 2016): 1206-1211. https://doi.org/10.1007/s11606-016-3703-5.

Saunders, J.B., OG Aaland, TF Babor, J.R. de la Fuente, M. Grant. " Development of the Alcohol Use Disorders Identification Test [AUDIT]: WHO Collaborative Project on Early Detection of Persons with Harmful Alcohol Consumption." Addiction 88, no.6 (June 1988): 791-804. https://doi.org/10.1111/j.1360-0443.1993.tb02093.x.

Spitzer, Robert, Kurt Kroenke, Janet B.W. Williams, Bernd Lowe. "A Brief Measure for Assessing Generalized Anxiety Disorder. *Archives of Internal Medicine* 166, no.10 (May 2006):1092-1097. https://doi:10.1001/archinte.166.10.1092.

Spitzer, R.L., K. Kroenke, J.B. Williams, "Validation and Utility of a Self-Report Version of PRIME-MD:the PHQ Primary Care Study. *Journal of the American Medical Association* 282, no. 18 (November 1999):1737-1744. https://doi.org/10.1001/jama.282.18.1737.

Healthy Minds Network. "Return on Investment Calculator for College Mental Health Services and Programs." Accessed on May 1, 2020. https://umich.qualtrics.com/jfe/form/SV_6xN-9QUSlFtgtRQh.

Youth Risk + Resilience Lab. "Home." Accessed on May 5, 2020. http://www.yr2lab.com/

Youth Risk + Resilience Lab. "Research." Accessed on May 5, 2020. http://www.yr2lab.com/

Zaslavsky. "Screening for Serious Mental Illness in the General Population." *Archives of General Psychiatry* 6, no. 2 (February 2003): 184-189. https://doi.org/10.1001/archpsyc.60.2.184

PART II: WHAT LEADERS IN THE FIELD ARE SAYING

Chapter 5: Providing Gold Standard Resources, Frameworks, and Programming

American Foundation for Suicide Prevention. "About AFSP." Accessed on May 13, 2020. https://afsp.org/about-afsp.

American Foundation for Suicide Prevention. "AFSP State Laws on Suicide Prevention on University and College Campuses." *AFSP Public Policy Office.* Washington, DC. June 7, 2019. Accessed on May 13, 2020. https://www.datocms-assets.com/12810/1576947491-afsphigher-ed-issue-brief6-7-19.pdf.

American Foundation for Suicide Prevention. "Interactive Screening Program." Accessed on May 13, 2020. https://afsp.org/interactive-screening-program.

American Foundation for Suicide Prevention. "The Overnight Walk Honor Beads." Accessed on May 13, 2020. https://afsp.org/about-afsp.

American Heart Association. "Lifestyle Changes for Heart Attack Prevention." Accessed on May 13, 2020. https://www.heart.org/en/health-topics/heart-attack/life-after-a-heart-attack/lifestyle-changes-for-heart-attack-prevention.

Cities Rise. "Local Collective Action," Accessed on May 1, 2020. http://cities-rise.org/citiesrise/.

The JED Foundation. "A Guide to Campus Mental Health Action Planning." Accessed on May 1, 2020. http://www.jedfoundation. org/wp-content/uploads/2016/07/campus-mental-health-action-planning-jed-guide.pdf.

The JED Foundation. "JED Story Tellers," Accessed on May 1,2020. https://www.jedfoundation.org/storytellers/.

The JED Foundation. "What We Do," Accessed on May 1, 2020. https://www.jedfoundation.org/what-we-do/.

The JED Foundation. "Who We Are." Accessed on May 1, 2020. https://www.jedfoundation.org/who-we-are/.

Chapter 6: Creating Hope Through Connectedness and Community

Active Minds. "Landmark Study Confirms Active Minds Has a Significant Impact on Student Mental Health and Well-Being." Accessed on May 3, 2020. https://www.activeminds.org/about-us/mission-and-impact/study/.

Sontag-Padilla, Lisa et al. "Strengthening College Students' Mental Health Knowledge, Awareness, and Helping Behaviors: The Impact of Active Minds, A Peer Mental Health Organization." *Journal of The American Academy of Child & Adolescent Psychiatry* 57, no7 (2018): 500-507. https://doi.org/10.1016/j.jaac.2018.03.019

NAMI. "Frequently Asked Questions." Accessed on May 14, 2020. https://www.nami.org/FAQ/General-Information-FAQ/What-does-NAMI-stand-for-and-what-is-its-mission.

NAMI. "Share Your Story." Accessed on May 14, 2020. https://www.nami.org/get-involved/share-your-story.

Chapter 7: A Public Health Perspective

American Association of Suicidology. "About ASS." Accessed on May 1, 2020. https://suicidology.org/about-aas/.

American Association of Suicidology. "Suicide Attempt Survivors." Accessed on May 1, 2020. https://suicidology.org/resources/suicide-attempt-survivors/.

National Action Alliance for Suicide Prevention. "Goals and Objectives." Accessed on May 15, 2020. https://theactionalliance.org/our-strategy/national-strateg/2012-national-strategy.

National Action Alliance for Suicide Prevention. "2012 National Strategy for Suicide Prevention: Goals and Objectives for Action: A Report of the U.S. Surgeon General and of the National Action Alliance for Suicide Prevention." https://www.ncbi.nlm.nih.gov/books/NBK109918/.

Suicide Prevention Resource Center. "National Data Shows Firefighters' Mental and Emotional Health Not Getting Enough Attention." Accessed on May 15, 2020 https://www.sprc.org/news/national-data-shows-firefighters%E2%80%99-mental-emotional-health-not-getting-enough-attention.

Chapter 8: A Social Justice Perspective

American Psychiatric Association. "APA President." Accessed on May 1, 2020. https://www.apa.org/about/governance/president.

American Foundation for Suicide Prevention. "It's Real:College Students and Mental Health. Accessed on May 1, 2020. https://afsp.org/its-real-college-students-and-mental-health.

Davis, Kelly. "How Can I Help a Friend Struggling with Their Mental Health?" *The BetterMynd Blog*. May 30, 2018. https://www.bettermynd.com/how-can-i-help-a-friend-struggling-with-their-mental-health/?fbclid=IwAR3SvZ7xBBhEL-WCR6304qko1A7qM1otAKoCl-DnZoUw_uu3ucEh3KbFr8pw.

Don't Deny Me. "Don't Be Denied: Your Right to Mental Health and Addiction Treatment." Accessed on May 1, 2020. https://pjk-wpuploads.s3.amazonaws.com/www.parityregistry.org/uploads/2018/10/DontDenyMe_Infographic.pdf.

Don't Deny Me. "Equal Access to Mental Health and Addiction Treatment Services is Your Right." Accessed on May 4, 2020. https://www.parityregistry.org/dont-deny-me/?utm_source=tkf&utm_medium=offline&utm_campaign=ddm.

Haegele, A. Justin, "Disability Discourse: Overview and Critiques of the Medical and Social Model." *Quest- Illinois-National Association for Physical Education in Higher Education* 68, no.2 (March 2016): 1-14. https://doi.org/10.1080/00336297.2016.1143849.

HanNa Lim, Stuart J. Heckman, Jodi C. Letkiewicz, Catherine P. Montalt. "Financial Stress, Self-Efficacy, and Financial

Help-Seeking Behavior of College Students." *Journal of Financial Counseling and Planning* 25, no. 2 (2014):148-160. https://files.eric.ed.gov/fulltext/EJ1048681.pdf

Herman, Christine. "How Racism, Trauma and Mental Health are Linked." *Side Effects Public Health Personal Stories.* February 22, 2019. https://www.sideeffectspublicmedia.org/post/how-racism-trauma-and-mental-health-are-linked

The Kennedy Forum. "How We'll Do It." Accessed on May1, 2020. https://www.thekennedyforum.org/vision/.

The Kenned Forum. "Parity Progress." Accessed on May 1, 2020. https://www.thekennedyforum.org/about/parity-progress/

Mental Health America. "About Mental Health America." Accessed on May 1, 2020.https://www.mhanational.org/about.

Mental Health America. "Position Statement 73: College and University Response to Mental Health Crises." Accessed on May 1, 2020 https://www.mhanational.org/issues/position-statement-73-college-and-university-response-mental-health-crises.

Ruriani.Alyse. "Dig Deeper Prints." Accessed on May 1, 2020. http://alyseruriani.com.

Chapter 9: Research, Implementation, and Dissemination

Eisenberg, Daniel and Sarah Ketcher Lipson. "The Healthy Minds Study: 2018-2019 Data Report." *Healthy Minds Network.* 1 – 10. https://healthymindsnetwork.org/wp-content/uploads/2019/09/HMS_national-2018-19.pdf.

Mindstrong. "Mental Health Care Made for You." Accessed on May 2, 2020. https://mindstronghealth.com/

Havard T.H. Chan School of Public Health. "Means Matter." Accessed on May 2, 2020. https://www.hsph.harvard.edu/means-matter/recommendations/colleges/.

RAND Gun Policy in America. "How Gun Policies Affect Outcomes: What the Evidence Shows Us." Accessed April 30, 2020. https://www.rand.org/research/gun-policy.html#latest-updates-april-2020-.

RAND Gun Policy in America. "The Effects of Child-Access Prevention Laws." Accessed April 30, 2020. https://www.rand.org/research/gun-policy/analysis/child-access-prevention.html.

Chapter 10: From the Front Lines: Counseling Center Directors

The Princeton Review. "The Princeton Review College Ranking Methodology." Accessed May 3, 2020. https://www.princetonreview.com/college-rankings/ranking-methodology.

American Foundation for Suicide Prevention. "Risk Factors and Warning Signs." Accessed May 4, 2020. https://afsp.org/risk-factors-and-warning-signs.

Brown University. "Helping a Student in Distress." Accessed on May 3, 2020. https://www.brown.edu/helping-a-student/how-can-i-help.

Brown University. "Labs." Accessed on May 6, 2020. https://www.brown.edu/campus-life/support/counseling-and-psychological-services/labs.

Cornell Health. "Let's Talk – Drop in Consultation." Accessed on May 2, 2020. https://health.cornell.edu/services/mental-health-care/lets-talk.

American Foundation for Suicide Prevention. "Suicide Statistics." Accessed on April 30, 2020. https://afsp.org/suicide-statistics/.

Center for Collegiate Mental Health. "2019 Annual Report." January, 2020. https://ccmh.psu.edu/files/2020/03/2019-CCMH-Annual-Report_3.17.20.pdf.

PART 3: MY LIVED EXPERIENCES

Chapter 11: Combining Spheres

Drug and Alcohol Research Education. "About D.A.R.E. America." Accessed on May 1, 2020. https://Dare.org/About.

Chapter 12: Breaking Stereotypes

Best Colleges. "Understanding Eating Disorders." Accessed on May 1, 2020. https://www.bestcolleges.com/resources/eating-disorders/.

Chansky, Tamar. *Freeing Your Child From Obsessive-Compulsive Disorder.* New York: Three Rivers Press, 2000.

Cornell Research Program for Self-Injury and Recovery Resources. "What is Self-Injury?" College of Human Ecology Cornell University. Accessed May 1,2020. http://www.selfinjury.bctr.cornell.edu/about-self-injury.html.

Crisis Text Line. "How to Deal with Self Harm?" Accessed on May 1,2020.

https://www.crisistextline.org/topics/self-harm/#recovering-from-self-harm-7.

International OCD Foundation. "How is OCD Treated?" Accessed on May 1, 2020. https://iocdf.org/about-ocd/ocd-treatment/.

International OCD Foundation. "What is OCD?" Accessed on May 1, 2020. https://iocdf.org/about-ocd/.

Klonsky, E. David, Catherine R. Glenn, Denise M. Styer, Thomas M. Olino, and Jason J.Washburn. "The Functions of Nonsuicidal Self-Injury: Converging Evidence for a Two-Factor Structure." *Child and Adolescent Psychiatry and Mental Health* 9, no. 1 (2015) https://doi.org/10.1186/s13034-015-0073-4.

Lewis, P. Stephen and Hasking, Penelope. "Putting the "Self" in Self-Injury Research: Inclusion of People with Lived Experience in the Research Process." *Psychiatric Services* 70, no.11 (2019): 1058-1060 https://doi.org/10.1176/appi.ps.201800488.

Peace of Mind. "What is OCD." Accessed on May 1,2020. https://peaceofmind.com/education/types-of-ocd/counting-checking/.

Psychiatry. "What is Obsessive Compulsive Disorder?" Accessed on May 1,2020. https://www.psychiatry.org/patients-families/ocd/what-is-obsessive-compulsive-disorder.

Shaefer, Jenni and Thom Rutledge. *Life Without Ed: How One Woman Declared Her Independence from Her Eating Disorder and How You Can Too*. New York: McGraw-Hill Education, 2004.

TLEX Institute. "Mind Matters: How to Effortlessly Have More Positive Thoughts." Accessed on May 1, 2020. https://tlexinstitute.com/how-to-effortlessly-have-more-positive-thoughts.

Viriginia Commission on Youth. "Collection of Evidence-based Practices for Children and Adolescents with Mental Health Treatment Needs." Published on 2017. http://vcoy.virginia.gov/documents/collection/025%20Nonsuicidal%20self%20injury2.pdf.

Whitlock, Janis, Stephen P. Lewis, Imke Baetens, and Penelope Hasking. "Non-Suicidal Self-Injury on College Campuses." *HigherEducationToday*. February 6, 2019. https://www.higheredtoday.org/2019/02/06/non-suicidal-self-injury-college-campuses/.

Chapter 13: Uncovering the Mask
Dickens, Charles. *A Tale of Two Cities*. New York: Chelsea House Publishing, 1987.

Soho, CBT and Mindfulness Center. "Acceptance and Commitment Therapy." Accessed on May 1,2020. http://www.sohocbt.com/act#.

Chapter 14: Recovery and Healing

Glasofer, Deborah. "5 Ways to Defuse Anxious Thoughts." Very Well Mind. Last modified March 25, 2020. https://www.verywellmind.com/ways-to-defuse-anxious-thoughts-3863037.

Kneff, Kristin. Center for Mindful Self-Compassion. "Definition and Three Elements of Self Compassion." Accessed on May 1, 2020. https://self-compassion.org/the-three-elements-of-self-compassion-2/#3elements.

Linehan, Marsha M. *DBT Skills Training Handouts and Worksheets.* 2nd ed. New York: Guildford Press, 2014.

Chapter 15: My Personal Why

Linehan, Marsha M. *DBT Skills Training Handouts and Worksheets.* 2nd ed. New York: Guildford Press, 2014.

PART 5: STUDENT VOICES AND CALL TO ACTION

Chapter 15: What Student Mental Health Advocates Are Saying

The Reflect Organization. "Who Are We?" Accessed on May 1, 2020. https://www.reflecteffect.org.

TEDx Talks, "How College Fails US: Reimagining Higher Education| Leah Goodman | TedxRushU," February 19, 2020, video, 16:23 https://www.youtube.com/watch?v=n9MeA6uejGU.

U.S. Department of Education, "About ED" Accessed in May 6, 2020. https://www2.ed.gov/about/landing.jhtml

Van Heeringen, K. "Stress Diathesis Model of Suicidal Behavior." The Neurobiological Basis of Suicide. CRC Press/Taylor & Francis. Chapter 6. 2012. Available from: https://www.ncbi.nlm.nih.gov/books/NBK107203/.

Chapter 16: Call to Action
Chugani, Carla. "DBT for College Students." Accessed on May 1, 2020. https://www.carlachugani.com/.

Dialetical Behavioral Therapy. "T10: TIPP." Accessed on May 15, 2020. https://dialecticalbehaviortherapy.com/distress-tolerance/tipp/.

Higher Education Mental Health Alliance. "Postvention: A Guide to Suicide Response on College Campuses." Accessed May 1, 2020. http://hemha.org/wp-content/uploads/2018/06/jed-hemha-postvention-guide.pdf.

Kirsch, Daniel, Stephanie L. Pinder-Amaker, Charles Morse, Marsha L. Ellison, Leonard A. Doerfler, Michelle B. Riba. "Population-Based Initiatives in College Mental Health: Students Helping Students to Overcome Obstacles." *Current Psychiatry Reports 16* (2014): 525. https://doi.10.1007/s11920-014-0525-1.

National Council for Behavioral Health. "Mental Health First Aid." Accessed on May 1, 2020. https://www.mentalhealthfirstaid.org.

Pistorello, Jacqueline, Alan E. Fruzzetti, and Chelsea MacLane. "Dialetical Behavior Therapy (DBT) Applied to College Students: A Randomized Clinical Trial." *Journal of Consulting and Clinical Psychology,* 80, no.6 (2019): 982 – 994. https://doi.10.1037/a0029096

QPR Institute. "Questions Persuade Refer." Accessed on May 1, 2020. https://qprinstitute.com.

TheraNest. "Therapy Tools & Resources for Mental Health Providers." Accessed on May 1, 2020. https://theranest.com/resources/.

USCCR. "Sharing the Dream: Is the ADA Accommodating All?" Accessed May 1, 2020. https://www.usccr.gov/pubs/ada/ch5.htm.

Chapter 19: A Letter to Future Student Mental Health Advocates
RESOURCES

Crisis Text Line. "In a Crisis?" Modified 2020. https://www.crisistextline.org/.

The Jed Foundation. "Mental Health Resource Center." Accessed on May 20, 2020. https://www.jedfoundation.org/mental-health-resource-center/.

Reportingonsuicide.org. "Recommendations for Reporting on Suicide." Accessed on May 6, 2020. https://reportingonsuicide.org/recommendations/.

Stanley, Barbara and Gregory K. Brown. "The Safety Plan Template." 2011. Reprinted with express, written permission from authors.

Substance Abuse and Mental Health Services Administration. "The National Suicide Prevention Lifeline." Accessed on May 1, 2020. https://suicidepreventionlifeline.org/.

Suicide Prevention Lifeline. "Patient Safety Plan Template." Accessed on May 4, 2020. https://suicidepreventionlifeline. org/wp-content/uploads/2016/08/Brown_StanleySafetyPlan-Template.pdf.

The Trevor Project. "About the Trevor Project." Accessed on May 1, 2020. https://www.thetrevorproject.org/about/.

Made in the USA
Middletown, DE
04 June 2021